# TOWARD
# THE UNKNOWN

TRI THONG DANG

# TOWARD THE UNKNOWN

## Martial Artist, What Shall You Become?

CHARLES E. TUTTLE COMPANY
Rutland, Vermont & Tokyo, Japan

Published by the Charles E. Tuttle Publishing
an imprint of Periplus Editions (HK) Ltd.

©1997 Charles E. Tuttle Publishing Co., Inc.

First edition, 1997
First reprint, 1998

LCC Card No. 96-61646
ISBN 0-8048-2099-6

Printed in Singapore

Distributed by:

*USA* **Charles E. Tuttle
Company, Inc.**
Airport Industrial Park
RR1 Box 231-5
North Clarendon, VT 05759
Tel: (802) 773-8930
Fax: (802) 773-6993

*Japan* **Tuttle Shokai Ltd.**
1-21-13 Seki
Tama-ku, Kawasaki-shi
Kanagawa-ken 214, Japan
Tel: (81) (44) 833-0225
Fax: (81) (44) 822-0413

*Southeast Asia*
**Berkeley Books Pte Ltd.**
5 Little Road #08-01
Singapore 536983
Tel: (65) 280 3320
Fax: (65) 280 6290

*Tokyo Editorial Office:*
2-6, Suido 1-chome,
Bunkyo-ku, Tokyo 112, Japan

*Boston Editorial Office:*
153 Milk Street, 5th Floor
Boston, MA 02109, USA

*Singapore Editorial Office:*
5 Little Road #08-01
Singapore 536983

Visit Tuttle Web on the Internet:
**http://www.tuttle.co.jp/~tuttle/**

# CONTENTS

# Acknowledgments

My view of the universe I owe to long-departed but forever-vibrant masters, great examples of lives dedicated to the harmony of the Tao—the Grand Master Chiu-chuk Kai of Hong Kong, and O-Sensei Morihei Ueshiba of Japan.

For my upbringing in a family focused on harmony, I am grateful to my late parents. I hold them and my beloved brothers and sisters forever in heartfelt honor and respect.

In addition, I very much appreciate the advice of my friend and editorial consultant Dr. Jonathan Pearce in the preparation of this book.

[Master Tri Thong Dang died October 12, 1995]

# Relation of Hexagrams to Chapters

The hexagrams which highlight each chapter of this book come from the *I-Ching*, or *Book of Changes*. The 64 hexagrams symbolize all possible interactions and forms of change. The two forces (*yin/yang*, or passive/active) are constantly interacting and suggest all things are forever complementary and inseparable. This is the foundation upon which the lessons of Master Lam rest. Below are brief definitions of the 14 hexagrams that relate to the chapters in this book.

1. That which has become corrupted by humankind can be cleansed through the virtuous acts of humankind.
2. After degeneration, healing begins.
3. The virtuous are gentle; it is their spirit that speaks and accomplishes.
4. The sincere practitioner may make the most rapid progress.
5. Barriers arise to be overcome.
6. If resolution of a problem is not yet achieved, resolution may yet be near.
7. The honorable and virtuous enjoy discussion and practice.
8. A new beginning always follows an ending.
9. The Master does not strive to achieve tranquillity, for in striving the heart can not be quiet.
10. One develops character gradually and by persevering.
11. Bringing the truth to light is worth the danger in the bringing.
12. One who adheres to no position is in no position to advise.
13. Growth does not necessarily involve forward motion.
14. When truth is recognized, then humankind is in accord with heaven.

# 1

# FROM UNBEATABLE TO VANQUISHED

"YOU MAY go now, Lam, back into the world," Master Tai-Anh said to his disciple.

Lam replied to himself, "Ah, but that is not at all what I wish to do." Lam, newly named Master by his aged teacher, had dreamt of remaining in seclusion, spending his life in meditation and self-improvement. But Master Tai-Anh had now changed that for Lam.

"Go into the world, Lam," Master Tai-Anh had said. "Go, and demonstrate your artistry there for the benefit of the people." So Lam made preparations to obey.

In spite of the direction he had been given, Lam was drawn to stay on Master Tai-Anh's island, taking care of the old man as long as Master Tai-Anh lived. He felt more than "drawn;" he felt an obligation and a responsibility.

He had given vent to his feelings to Master Tai-Anh

on several occasions. "I do wish to remain with you Master," he had said several times, justifying his sentiment with rational argument. However, the old Master did not reply, and Lam felt constrained to continue his preparations to depart.

When it had become obvious that Lam was feeling truly depressed at the prospect of abandoning the old man, Master Tai-Anh relented. "You may stay until it is absolutely time for you to go," said the Master. "You will know that time when it arrives, and it will be soon."

Lam was elated. He had gained yet another opportunity to study with Master Tai-Anh, and continue listening to the Master's discourse. He and his master could continue to debate fine points of philosophy, and could commiserate about news brought by the occasional visitor to the island of the awful upheavals their native land was enduring. He could continue for a time to breathe in the essence of the art of a supreme martial artist. And during the next three months, this opportunity that Lam had hoped for did take place.

But one morning when Lam arrived at the Master's room with the morning tea, Master Tai-Anh was gone, to appear no more that day, that week, or that month. He had simply vanished, leaving his few worldly goods behind. Lam had no fears that Master Tai-Anh might have met foul play, for in Lam's experience there was no one who could best the Master. But Lam did come to a disturbing conclusion.

Lam believed that the Master's disappearance must

be another of his "tricks." This time a stratagem to stimulate Lam to cut off what Master Tai-Anh would have
described as "petty personal sentiment"—any emotional
attachment of Lam to the Master which might hinder
Lam from performing his duty. The more Lam thought
about this, the more firmly he was convinced that the
Master had indeed gone away for good, departing in
this eccentric way as his final gift to Lam. Lam's eyes
filled with tears, but he then quickly resolved to follow
what he believed was the Master's intention and left the
island with a clear conscience and as little show of sentiment as he could manage.

So Lam, "Master Lam," as Master Tai-Anh had appointed him, returned to society to fulfill his original
intention. He would follow Master Tai-Anh's will. He
had assured his Master that the gift that was now tucked
into Lam's belt, Master Tai-Anh's favorite sword, would
not be used the way an ordinary sword might be employed. The sword would do constructive deeds, the
purest of deeds, and never be used as an instrument of
destruction. It would serve as a symbol of justice, love,
and compassion. He resolved anew never to dishonor
Master Tai-Anh's teachings.

Returning to society, Lam was astounded by the
changes time had wrought in the country during his
absence. The most obvious and unpleasant changes were
revealed in the dress of the people. Their garb was no
longer simple and modest. Many of the women wore
gaudy apparel that revealed more of their bodies than

Lam thought seemly. The men wore blue jeans carelessly. Everyone was in a hurry, speaking hastily and revealing attitudes less tactful, less courteous, less decent than in years gone by.

As for the children of the city, Lam was horrified to see them footloose on the streets during the hours they should have been attending school, their faces emaciated, their clothing tattered. During the years that Lam had been on Master Tai-Anh's island, the country had indeed suffered significant changes—none for the better, it seemed.

Lam sat on a bench at a crossroads for a long while, observing the tumultuous scene. Things had really degenerated beyond his imagination. Lam lamented, "Manners and habits change with the times, but how can the change have come so fast and so far!" Disappointed, Lam shook his head and emitted a long sigh.

Lam remembered that Master Tai-Anh had said that a destructive new spirit, an unavoidable wave of alien materialism, was crashing on the shores of their country, turning the people's way of life upside down. Lam now saw that his Master's words were, as usual, accurate.

As Lam pondered he heard his name spoken, then shouted. Roused from his reverie, he turned finally and recognized his old classmate Hau Le. Lam could hardly forget Hau, for he was the martial arts student who had defeated Lam many times. Lam recalled especially those humiliating occasions after Lam had judged himself master of some new technique, bragged loudly about his personal skill and martial attributes, and then found himself whipped by Hau.

Hau's gown now had but one sleeve. The recently-concluded civil war in which Hau had lost his arm had foreclosed Hau's martial arts vocation along with the vocations, homes, institutions, and lives of several million of his countrymen. Hau no longer considered possible his pursuit of a martial arts teaching career.

"Come with me to the inn here, and we shall reminisce, old friend," said Hau, taking Lam by the elbow and leading him through the gateway to the inn. Seated over tea, the old adversaries exchanged news of events over the twenty-five years of their separation. Hau was especially interested in the disappearance of their beloved Master Tai-Anh. At length, they both fell silent, saddened by the absolute passing of the old life and recalling the advice of the Master.

Hau raised his head, a cheerful smile suddenly on his face. "Lam," he said, "I have a son, a beautiful youngster. I am so proud of him."

"I am truly pleased for you, Hau," replied Lam. "How old is the child and what are your hopes and expectations for him?"

"Xuan [pronounced "shwahn"] is nine. My friend, now that I see you before me and recall once again our Master's influence on our lives—and recognize in your every aspect those noble principles of martial art—I cannot think of anything I want more for my child than for him to follow you as your disciple as I tried to follow Master Tai-Anh."

Lam swallowed hard and bowed his head. "I am honored," he said.

"I am honored, Lam. For it seems that of all the people I know, you are the one who has maintained that balance that Master Tai-Anh said we should all strive for—that equipoise of body, mind, and spirit. I can see it in your eyes, hear it in your voice, see it in your bearing." Hau then led Lam to the Le home and bade him rest in the garden while Hau entered to let his wife and son know of the arrival of an honored guest.

Young Xuan had earlier returned from his game of soccer and was at the table eating a snack prepared by his mother. "Son," Hau said to the child as he entered, "I have been thinking about you and your development as a person and about your future."

Xuan looked interested.

"I have decided," continued Hau, "that you shall give up soccer and instead study martial arts."

Xuan stopped chewing and looked first at Hau and then at his mother and then back at Hau. Xuan was inordinately fond of soccer and spent a great deal of time playing the game with his friends. The thought of losing such joy almost caused him to burst into tears. But he did not, for obedience to King, teacher, father— part of the Confucian ethic—had been imbued in him from birth, and the father's deciding the son's future was not considered "unfair" or "an unequal distribution of power," or some other modern social argument. The father's decision must not be criticized in any way:

The father had considered, the father had spoken, and the father would be obeyed.

"I believe it will be good for you and good for the country for you to study martial arts," continued Hau. He looked closely at his child whose eyes now were filled with tears. "Xuan, don't grieve. Perhaps I was being a bit too severe. It is all right for you to continue playing soccer—along with studying martial arts."

Xuan's face brightened. He finally swallowed his snack.

"But," continued Hau, "I do not want to see you missing any kung-fu class. And, of course, your school work must be completed first, before either kung-fu or soccer. You do understand that, don't you?"

Xuan's reply was simple and direct. "Yes, Father." Hau retired to the garden to resume his conversation with Master Lam. Xuan then apparently returned his attention to finishing his snack, but his thoughts were in a whirl.

"Remember, Xuan," said the child's mother, "that your father has thought long and hard about this decision, what your father has asked you to do is for your own good. When you grow up, you will understand his reasoning. Do not be angry with his decision. Now, take a nap, son, and later we shall have a nice dinner."

A few weeks later, after Master Lam had taken up his residence in town, Xuan was called to prepare a welcoming gift for his kung-fu teacher. This tradition called for the disciple-to-be to present a gift at his first interview. The gift readied by Xuan consisted of two bottles of *mai-que-lo*, a special wine for the occasion, and a copper tray on which piled high was a variety of foods: chicken, roast pork, fruit, and confections of several kinds—all covered with a red cloth.

As Xuan made the presentation, his father formally introduced him to Master Lam and asked Lam to be Xuan's Master. Hau spoke with much ceremony, but Xuan remembered only the words, ". . . do what you will, treat him as you see fit." Hau demonstrated his complete trust in the judgment of the Master. Master Lam would be expected to be Xuan's surrogate father throughout the crucial development phase of the youth's life. Master Lam would be in authority over all aspects of Xuan's existence.

Xuan also recalled that he was directed not to talk about his training or demonstrate to anyone outside the school what he had learned there. The Master was particularly emphatic about that point: the confidentiality of the training.

Master Lam then said, "Tomorrow and every afternoon thereafter I will be here at five o'clock. Be on time with the other students." After a pause he solemnly continued, "I will make of you a man, a real human being."

Master Lam was now in his late fifties, very healthy, alert, soft of speech but with a somewhat stern expression. As Master Lam spoke, even his expression made great impression on little Xuan.

"Why does he want to make of me a real man?" said

Xuan to himself. "I am Xuan Le. Am I not already real?" Xuan reasoned: "I am now a boy, but in a matter of time I will naturally grow up and become a man—without the assistance of anyone. Will I become an unreal man without Master Lam?" Xuan was confused.

Xuan had confided his concern to his mother, and her answer was ambiguous. She had talked about things like human-heartedness and righteousness and chivalry, integrity, loyalty, honor to king and country. Those kinds of things, all strange and unfamiliar things, sounded grand but made little sense to Xuan. Mother kept saying things like, "You will understand this when you are older," or "You will understand what your father means when you are a man," or "Remember, what your father has asked of you is for your own good."

Throughout his early years of discipleship, Xuan thought about the words of his father and mother. The cardinal virtues of the human being—human-heartedness, righteousness, integrity, chivalry, loyalty, and honor to king and country—became, little by little, more meaningful as his experiences identified them. By the age of sixteen, and after almost eight years of studying with Master Lam, Xuan showed clearly some of the traits of authentic adulthood. Whenever he thought of his parents, he smiled, for the expression "It is for your own good" actually was beginning to make sense.

Early one Sunday morning a rough, robust man apparently in his early thirties arrived at Master's Lam residence. He pulled the rope on the bell at the gate and almost at once Xuan appeared to greet the visitor. The visitor was a self-taught man with great native talent who had become accomplished in the martial arts and was considerably full of himself. In a most haughty tone he commanded the youth to present him to Master Lam. "I would speak now with your Master," he said. "Now!" he repeated.

"At this moment my Master is engaged and must not be disturbed," said Xuan calmly, now well-trained in how to greet visitors with polite expressions, but taken aback by this visitor's rudeness. "May I take your name to report to him when he is free?"

With an oath, the man pushed Xuan aside and strode to the central hall where he found Master Lam sitting on the mat engaged in calligraphy, his enormous brush flying over a long white sheet of paper, his gestures sweeping. Master Lam ignored the intruder who stood over him, hands on his hips.

As Master Lam continued his writing without looking up, the man said to him in a loud voice, "I have heard that you give lessons in martial arts and that you have many followers. You must be reasonably good if you have lots of followers, so I have come to receive your teaching." He then waited for a reply.

Realizing that this was not a friendly application, but a challenge, Master Lam stopped writing, put aside his brush, and responded. Smiling but not raising his eyes to meet those of the intruder, he said, "Ah! You are also a martial artist. May I know your name and the name of your Master?"

The man snorted. "Master?" he said. "I am my own

Master. I have taught myself to become expert in the use of eighteen types of weapons. I have invented my own principles and techniques. I have never found it necessary to be guided by anybody. And my name? Because never in my life have I been defeated by anybody, you may call me "Unbeatable." The man strode about the room, examining the artifacts displayed on the wall, and continued to brag about his ability, about his defeating several eminent masters, about the invincible nature of his techniques.

Master Lam listened politely. When the man seemed to have run out of brag and breath, Master Lam spoke. "You say you have had no Master. I find that most interesting for I wonder, without a Master, how is one able to enter the essence of the art? Who but one's Master is able to guide a person to becoming a whole man or woman?"

The challenger opened his mouth as if to answer, but Master Lam smiled politely and held up his hand. "I myself," he said, "have never prided myself on being a 'famous martial arts master' or 'famous' anything else. So there is no need for you to make a big fuss over me and my reputation. I'm sure you are just being kind." Master Lam's voice became quieter and he raised his eyes to the man for the first time, looking directly at him as he spoke, "I am not a 'famous' man, but I do have some knowledge of the fighting arts."

"Well, that's too bad," said The Unbeatable. "I mean, it's too bad that you are not one of the more capable martial arts Masters. So I'm wasting my time coming here. Well, that's that. Pity." So saying, he turned his back and would have left at once.

Smiling broadly, the Master spoke up. "Don't be in such a hurry. Our chat is not over yet."

"You will accept my request?"

"Of course," said the Master, "but try one of my students first. When you have succeeded in defeating him, it won't be too late for us to engage in business." Master Lam smiled engagingly.

The Unbeatable tossed his head and thrust out his lip, frowning. "I have already thrashed a number of very illustrious opponents. I'll not have my reputation soiled by some clumsy, insignificant disciple."

The Master said softly, "Well, if you so insist, you may try your luck against me. However, I shall impose a condition."

The challenger rolled his eyes and snorted.

"If you accept the condition," continued the Master, "we shall have our contest. If you lose, you . . ."

The man interrupted impatiently. "You are about to say that should I lose, I become your student and obey your every order and comply with all your rules, and that sort of thing." The Unbeatable folded his arms and shook his head, as if in exasperation at even the thought that he should lose.

"Exactly!" replied the Master with a delighted smile. "You have said exactly what I was about to say. We are on the same path after all."

The Unbeatable stifled a guffaw at the thought of his losing to this old man. Why, with a wave of his hand he could incapacitate this old bumbler and render him incapable of withstanding a second blow. "Conditions, rules, whatever, it doesn't matter a bit," sneered The Unbeatable. "I accept all. Let's have no more idle talk, for I have an appointment in the city in an hour. Let's begin!" So saying, he leaped to the court, landing in a combat-ready position.

The Master, composed as usual, arose slowly and stepped out holding his shoulder-height staff. Suddenly and with no visible effort he flung the staff to the man with a force so intense as to render the challenger's hands numb as he caught the staff. At that, a vagrant thought, disconcerting, entered the man's mind.

"I am ready," said Master Lam.

"You have thrown me a possible weapon, but you have none. Which weapon will you choose?" the challenger demanded.

Smiling, the Master raised his hands. "These two arms will suffice," he said.

The man argued. "In that case the fight will not be considered fair, and people will say I didn't win fair and square."

"Well, if you insist," said Master Lam and, taking a hand-fan out of his sash, he made the first move.

The challenger was forced to wave his staff, parry, and riposte. The Master warded off the counterattack, but the challenger immediately launched a forceful thrust toward the Master's throat, missing the target but succeeding in taking the offensive in several directions.

Each time, however, again and again the staff continued missing its mark. Suddenly the challenger perceived the Master to be vulnerable. Reversing the staff, the man thrust the weapon at the Master's lower body, aiming at the genitals with all his might. Again the staff pierced only air. At the same moment, the Master, using his fan in a deflecting technique, hurled his opponent's staff into the air, and it fell on the ground fifteen feet away.

At that, the challenger would have been wise to acknowledge defeat, but obstinacy and arrogance compelled him to try hand-to-hand combat. The Master returned the fan to his sash, responding to the challenger's nonverbal demand.

The challenger then vigorously attempted his most advanced techniques, while the Master, acting like a drunkard, calmly inclining now to the right, and then to the left, dodged all attacks gracefully. All at once the Master, moving with lightning speed, got behind the man and placed his hand on the man's shoulder.

The challenger suddenly felt as if he were carrying an extremely heavy weight. A tingling and numbness immobilized his arm. He tried to move the arm, but could not move it at all. He stood still, finally, his head lowered, panting with the effort and the humiliation, saying not a word, recognizing and accepting total defeat.

At once Master Lam ordered his disciples to set the altar for the defeated challenger to take a vow to become a novice. The Master said no word but indicated to the novice that he must kneel and accept the bowl of burning incense, which the novice held, raised over his head, and bowed deeply as a senior disciple pronounced aloud the unwritten rules of the school.

The Master then awarded the novice a new name, no longer "The Unbeatable," but now "The Vanquished." He was allowed to leave the school, but directed to return within a month. With an end to his arrogance and conceit, The Vanquished began a new life.

Following the ceremony, Master Lam left the court and followed a trail that led him to some woods. And while he strolled leisurely on that tranquil morning, he thought of the game that The Vanquished had just played and lost, a game that he himself had played with similar results when he had first met Master Tai Anh. As Master Lam recalled his own foolish behavior so many years before, the more ashamed he felt.

Master Lam's stroll took him shortly to the river where, sitting on a rock he watched the peacefully flowing water. This same river led to the island fifty miles away where he had lived with Master Tai Anh. Since his Master's disappearance he had heard nothing from the old man. He did not know if his old Master were alive or dead, and grief mixed with love flooded over him, tears coursed from his eyes.

"Master, wherever you are," Master Lam mumbled, "please witness this vow of your disciple. I will put all my heart and soul in the mission you entrusted me with. I will do my best!" As he finished intoning the last word, Master Lam seemed to hear a voice within him say,

"Don't be so weak, Master Lam! Don't be so weak. Otherwise, you will neglect your duty!"

He was at once infused with power and arose and took several deep breaths. He opened his eyes and was aware of the beauty around him. He swung his arms, performing a series of hand-sets in the t'ai-mantis kung-fu system—the *dan-zhai mei-hua, lan-jie, zhai-yao* routines—which engendered in him great *ch'i*. Then he whispered to himself one of the statements that Master Tai-Anh used to make during class: "One must have an unfailing energy and exercise unfailing will-power to handle important duties."

It was now noon, the sun high overhead. Master Lam, refreshed, optimistic, energized, walked leisurely back to his residence, a confident smile on his lips.

# 2

# USEFULNESS
# AND USELESSNESS

WITH THE Vanquished now gone to settle his affairs before his honor-required return to assume novice duties at the school, Xuan and the whole group of students were trying to deal with their feelings of hostility and animosity toward The Vanquished. The day after the contest that demonstrated the fallibility of The Vanquished, students dared to ask Master Lam his reasoning for admitting that arrogant and useless man to their beloved school.

Master Lam said of The Vanquished, "He is arrogant, yes; useless, no. I expect you to work with him according to how you perceive his capacity and his demeanor. Treat him as you would treat a piece of wood." The students exhibited puzzlement. "Do you remember that piece of rotten wood and the crooked rattan pole we found in the woods?" So saying, he retired to the garden where he thought again about his own youthful foolishness.

In the hall, the students tried to recreate Master Lam's example of the rotten wood and the crooked pole. A few months ago, while Master Lam and the students were strolling in the woods, the Master picked up a piece of wood and a warped pole lying on the trail and asked the youngsters to carry both back to the school.

Upon their return to the school, the students brought the items to Master Lam. "Master," they said, "this is but a dirty, worm-eaten piece of wood. And also, what should we do with this crooked rattan pole? Both are absolutely useless. What in the world shall we do with them?"

"Ah," said Master Lam, "look at them! Because of their appearance they do not please your eyes, and you assert immediately that they are 'useless.' Isn't that what you think? That they are 'useless'?"

The students were quiet. From experience they knew that they were about to receive a lesson.

"You look at things superficially and heedlessly and then consider those things unworthy. Well, in so doing you commit a common mistake in judgment—common but serious. Do you know that?" The Master took the wood in his hands, observed it closely, saying, "Judge nothing, judge nobody by appearance."

The disciples looked at one another silently.

"Appearance often deceives us," said the Master. "Look at this wood you reject. It is in fact very rare and precious stuff. It is *cam-lai* wood." He looked up at the group. "And if one knows how to make it useful, then you must agree, it will no longer be 'useless.' Is that not correct?"

Nods of agreement.

The Master bade the students be seated and then he took some instruments and began to chop and cut and scrape the dirty wood until gradually it took on the shape of a sword. He continued to scrape it again and again, rubbing it and polishing the carved *cam-lai* wood. Under the hands of the Master and before their eyes, the piece of dirty wood found in the forest became a beautiful wooden sword that a martial artist might use in training.

While cleaning up the mess created by the Master in his sword-making activity, Xuan and the other students commented enthusiastically on his creation. They swept up the wood shavings and cuttings and were about to throw them away when the Master stopped them, saying, "Do not throw these away. Nothing in this world is 'useless.' Nothing is 'useless.'" So saying, Master Lam picked a short scrap from the pile of cuttings and began once again to cut and scrape. Before long he had fashioned a wooden knife for use in training.

Master Lam then took some of the slimmer scraps, and of them he made letter openers. Of the smaller pieces yet, he carved various fasteners and pegs. Of the smallest pieces he fashioned toothpicks.

Impressed, the students said, "Now may we clean up and throw away the shavings and dust here?"

"You may not. Let me show you something else,"

and as he spoke, Master Lam gathered every scrap of the shavings and wood dust and piled them up in small heaps. Then after lighting one of the piles of shavings he took the crooked rattan pole and rolled it around and around in the heat of the small fire. When one small fire burned out Master Lam lighted another and repeated the rolling, gradually taking the curl out of the pole. Within half an hour, after successive heat treatments, Master Lam had a straight rattan pole, a training staff.

Xuan and the other students were amazed throughout the Master's demonstration. "Nothing is useless, everything is useful," the Master had said, and Xuan kept repeating the Master's words in his mind. "Do not judge anything, do not judge anyone, by appearance. And remember that each individual is different. If you do not require or expect that everyone behave like you, then you may find that everyone can be useful to the degree of his or her capacity." By means of the piece of wood and the crooked pole, Master Lam had communicated some complex ideas, and Xuan began to comprehend more of the examples, the metaphors, and the allegoric attitude.

The announcement of admittance of The Vanquished to the school was an objective lesson for the students. The Master intended to use his eccentric teaching methods to straighten the crooked and unsound behavior of his student-to-be. Master Lam intended for The Vanquished to become not only a competent martial artist, but a useful citizen and contributing member of society.

Of course, whether or not The Vanquished returned to the school was up to him. If he were truly able to set aside his ego and fulfill his word, then this action in itself might change his life for the better. If he did not keep his vow, he would thereafter be known as a coward, despised by all martial arts adepts, for he would have violated one of the basic tenets of the Asian martial arts legacy: One keeps one's promises. The Vanquished would determine his course of action, his own way of life.

Master Lam considered how he could underscore the lesson for his students, and he recalled Chuang Tsu's tale about usefulness and uselessness. Gathering the students about him, the Master recounted the tale.

Pham-Lai left Viet-Cau-Tien and moved first to the State of Te and later yet settling in the State of Dao. There he became a millionaire. People called him Dao-Chu-Cong and he was considered happy and wise, as well as rich. However, his second son who was living in the State of So committed a crime, was arrested, and imprisoned.

Dao-Chu-Cong gathered ten thousand ingots of his gold and sent for his youngest son, gave him the gold, and ordered him to go to the rescue of his brother. The oldest son, the first son, asked his father if he might go instead of the youngest son.

"I am the oldest son," said the first son. "It is customary for the oldest son to assume responsibility to go on such a mission." But the father denied the oldest son's request, even though it was repeated again and again with considerable lamentation. After repeated requests and repeated refusals, the oldest son felt himself humiliated, out of place, useless. He gave every appearance that he was about to kill himself out of shame.

Seeing this, the mother intervened. "You must not allow our oldest son to die for such a reason," she said to the father. The father reluctantly relented, and sent for the oldest son. He gave the son carefully phrased instructions, delivered most emphatically and seriously: "When you arrive in the State of So, deliver this letter and present this gold to Mister Trang-Sinh. Do not match wits with him. Do not try to do better than he. Do not circumvent him. Remember, do not match wits with him. He knows how to handle this problem. Leave the whole affair to him!"

The oldest son left home with his father's ten thousand ingots, and also with a few hundred ingots of his own gold. Upon arriving at Mr. Trang-Sinh's modest house, located in a rural area, the oldest son delivered the letter and presented the gold to Mr. Trang-Sinh.

"Very good," Old Trang-Sinh said. "It will be all right. I will look into it. Now you must immediately return home. Do not remain here longer. If your brother is released, do not ask how or why."

The oldest brother did take his leave, but only from the immediate area. He said to himself, "This old man is toothless and weak. Surely my father has made a great mistake in trusting to him my father's gold and the welfare of my brother. I am neither toothless nor weak.

I will see what I can do." And he thereupon remained in the State of So and used some of his personal gold to bribe an official who he thought had some power and influence in the So government.

The "toothless and weak" Mr. Trang-Sinh did indeed live a simple life as an ordinary citizen in a rural area. But he was known for his integrity, honesty, righteousness, and simplicity. Not only did people in the country respect him, but the King of So himself also showed him regard and consideration.

Trang-Sinh was granted an audience with the King and informed his liege: "My King, I must tell you that this humble subject has seen a dark shadow on the star of Mo. I regret to say that this sign appears to bode evil for the nation."

"Ah, woe," said the King of So. "What then should we do?"

"Only by employing all your virtue can Your Majesty suppress this evil," replied Trang-Sinh.

The King responded, "All right. I will follow your advice," and he therefore gave the order to seal up the treasury.

The official who had been bribed by the oldest son of Dao-Chu-Cong reported to that oldest son. "The King is going to grant amnesty."

"How do you know," the oldest son inquired.

The official replied, "Each time the King grants amnesty, he usually first orders the treasury sealed."

Dao's oldest son thought, "If the King grants amnesty, then naturally my brother will be released. What a pity that I gave that old man ten thousand gold ingots. How useless now to have given that gold!"

And he went straightaway to Mr. Trang-Sinh, who was most surprised to see him. "Ah! You are still here then," said the old man.

"Yes, Sir," said the oldest son, "I am still here. I hear my younger brother will enjoy the amnesty that the King is about to declare, so I just came by to, mm, ah, say thank you for you efforts, and to, mm, ah, well, to return home, just as soon as my brother is released."

Mr. Trang-Sinh understood the unspoken message, the intent of the oldest son to retrieve the gold he had brought from his father. "Well, go inside and take the gold back to your father Dao-Chu-Cong," he said.

So the oldest son did, smiling broadly, overjoyed in recovering the property. The oldest son then celebrated the imminent release of his brother.

But Mr. Trang-Sinh, who had intended all along to return the gold to Dao-Chu-Cong, now felt humiliated by the duplicity of the oldest son. He arranged to have another audience with the King. This time he said to the King, "Your Majesty, the other day I reported to you of the dark shadow on the star of Mo, interpreted that it boded evil for the state, and suggested that your exercise of Kingly virtue would make things right."

"Yes, I believe I have identified a way that a virtuous use of my power, a general amnesty, may be exercised to benefit many of our people." The King seemed very much pleased.

"Ah, Your Majesty," said Mr. Trang-Sinh in a sad voice, "I must report that I have recently heard a rumor that distresses me greatly. It seems that Dao-Chu-Cong, a wealthy merchant in the State of Dao, has a son who lives in the State of So. That son has committed murder and is imprisoned here." Mr. Trang-Singh looked down and shook his head as he continued. "The son's family brought gold here to bribe the officials of Your Majesty's Government so that those officials might free the son." Mr. Trang-Sinh opened his hands before him as if in perplexity and looked at the King. "Now it is spoken in the streets," he said, "that it may be Dao-Chu-Cong's gold rather than Your Majesty's love for his people that will have caused this amnesty."

The King drew in his breath sharply. "This is intolerable," he said. He became more and more angry, and soon issued an order for the immediate execution of the second son of Dao-Chu-Cong. The beheading of the second son of Dao-Chu-Cong was performed in short order, and on the day after the execution, the King granted a general amnesty.

When news of the execution reached the State of Dao, the people of Dao were shocked by the news. The mother of the youth grieved, her pain being great. But Dao-Chu-Cong only smiled bitterly. When asked why he did not wail and rend his garments in grief, he said, "Let me explain," and thereupon he remarked to his friends as follows:

"I had a feeling that this would happen if I relented.

Alas, I suspected that my oldest son's actions might kill his brother, and yet because of his position in the family I felt I must show trust in him. That is the source of my bitterness. This tragedy occurred not because my first son had no regard for his brother. He did love his brother dearly. But he could not bear to lose the gold."

"Please explain how this could have happened," said the friends.

Dao-Chu-Cong continued his explanation. "I am wealthy now, but I have not always been so, and when my children were younger, our family endured great hardship. Because he is the oldest, my sad first-born has recalled those early hardships more vividly than the other children. When he was a young adult, he had much difficulty in earning a living. For these reasons he became stingy and close with money, never spending a cent if it could be avoided.

"Now, his younger brother, the youngest of all my children, never knew hardship, for as he grew, my fortunes improved and so did those of the younger children. The youngest brother never learned how painful it can be to make a living or where, indeed, wealth originates. He therefore spends money like water and treats wealth generally with contempt.

"Initially, I sent for the youngest son to go to save the second-oldest, precisely because the youngest treats money with such contempt. I actually chose him for this reason. The oldest son, on the other hand, with his consuming interest in money, insisted that it was his duty and right to go to save my second son. I relented, saved his face, and lost my second son. Well, that's life. Pitiable, yes, but that's life, too. My only hope now is that will be able to bring his brother's body home."

Upon concluding this tale, Master Lam expounded on his anecdote, to be sure that all understood the point of the story. "This is a lesson in 'usefulness' and 'uselessness,'" he said. "Whereas the oldest son was useful in making money and getting it to grow, the youngest son was useless in that. However, to save the second son's life, the youngest son was useful and the oldest, useless. But remember, to the mature mind, what is important is not what is useful or useless, but how one may use one's skill and knowledge in a timely manner."

# 3

# Technique Versus Mind

Eight years passed. Xuan was now in his seventeenth year. Though throughout his novitiate he had experienced the usual joys and sorrows of growing up, he always delighted in the training.

One morning Hau watched as Xuan performed some of the hand sets of tai-mantis kung-fu in the backyard of his home. From the doorway Hau said, "Xuan, your movements seem to lack something vital." Xuan did not understand the point, and appeared not only puzzled but also a bit miffed at the criticism. Hau stepped into the yard and said, "Come, attack me." Out of respect for his father, Xuan hesitated. But Hau pressed him, "Come on, punch me, kick me, then I will show your weakness, your deficiency."

Compelled by his father's order, Xuan punched and kicked at Hau, but the punching and kicking were not vigorous, for how dare a son try to do harm to his own disabled father?

"You must try with real force!" shouted Hau. "I shall not break."

Xuan then threw real punches and on-target kicks, but the blows did not seem to affect Hau at all. Hau simply stood immobile, firmly planted on the ground like a stone pillar. Xuan frowned in puzzlement. Then with a single palm-strike Hau attacked Xuan's pectoral area, and the blow lifted Xuan from his feet and he fell to the ground.

While Xuan lay bewildered by this strange turn of events, his father said, "Son, your punches and kicks are swift and accurate but they lack vitality."

Being in the midst of adolescence, Xuan relied solely on his physical prowess to provide swift and accurate activity. He was still unaware of that mysterious invisible energy that crowns the art as understood by its mature practitioners. It belongs chiefly in the realm of mental and spiritual activity about which most youngsters are ignorant or apathetic and virtually unconcerned. Hau saw clearly his son's immaturity. However, he felt it necessary to begin to demonstrate this abstract dimension of spirituality so as to provide Xuan with at least a hint of that phenomenon which he had just demonstrated.

Xuan lay on the ground, looking at his father with respect and puzzlement mixed with humiliation at being bested by someone "old" with such a disability.

"Xuan," Hau said, turning and entering the house.

"Come inside now and listen attentively to a story I will tell you. This tale might help clarify your perplexity." Father and son then sat and Hau began his story. Xuan listened most attentively.

"Long ago in my youthful years," began Hau, "I witnessed two men in their thirties in an inn disputing over the time-honored question 'Which is more important in the art of fighting—mind or technique?' The men belonged to two different schools of martial arts, one famous in the North and the other renowned in the South. Each had claimed loudly his school to be the foremost. The discussion had become more and more heated and culminated in a duel to decide their claims.

"I was at that time bewildered at the ferocity of the arguing and worried for the safety of the men," said Hau. "I didn't realize then that such an argument, although very common, is a dangerous thorn in the thicket of martial arts."

"Father, why can't people learn to live in harmony, instead of disputing over such a stupid question?" Xuan asked.

"Ah, son, that's the way ignorant people have done things over the centuries—'ignorant' in that they have not reached the spiritual maturity necessary to live in cooperation. Instead they continue to seek out conflict and competition. But let me finish the story first, then we can discuss it."

"In the first of their encounters to decide which of the schools was the better, the combat did not last long. The man belonging to the school advocating mastery of technique easily defeated the man who supported the school of the mind. Although badly bruised, the man of the mindschool still firmly maintained that his school was the better. He said loudly that he was defeated only because he had not had enough years of training. He insisted that another match should take place in three years. The opponent sneered at the excuse but accepted the challenge.

"Three years later the men met again in the same spot. This time the fighting lasted for hours, and the man of technique revealed signs of fatigue. He discovered that he had ceased to be the master of his actions and would fall if the combat were to continue and he could even die under his opponent's sword. This time it was the man of technique who proposed to adjourn the fight to a later date, and the deferral was accepted.

"Three years later, the two rivals met yet again. This time, word of the competition had spread far and wide and the public rushed to the woods to witness the conclusion. The two began in the art of pugilism. After hours of hand-to-hand combat, the man of technique was defeated. The contest continued in the afternoon employing the art of swordsmanship. The watchers all expected a spectacle of fighting skill between the two warriors. But to the amazement of all, the two combatants did not rush at each other, swords flashing. Instead, they stood motionless at the ready, maintaining defensive postures, hands on sword hilts, neither attempting to draw their sword.

"Many minutes elapsed. The members of the crowd

did not dare speak, but only watch, eyes moving from one fighter to the other. Finally, the man of mind felt in his opponent a sign of trepidation and an expression of spiritual imbalance. The man of mind slowly released his hand from the hilt, turned, and left the scene. Suddenly he heard a click and the slow hiss of his opponent's sword being drawn, for the man of technique was preparing to stab himself out of humiliation. The man of mind turned and quickly intervened to stop the self-destruction.

"Without launching any attack, the man of the school of mind had defeated his opponent. The public marveled at this situation.

"Father," said Xuan, "I don't understand."

Father Hau said, "Yes, it is not easy to understand what happened in that 'fight,' but your understanding of the phenomenon is vital if you are to attain martial artistry. Listen, my son, in actual combat, every physical movement and every feature of one's mental and spiritual state is distilled out of one's own martial past. But if during combat you allow yourself to review your experience or speculation on your future, your participation in the flow of universal energy will be interrupted. That flow will end and you will be rendered incapable.

"The true 'technique' is not recognizable as such at all. It has no specific movement, no scheme, no plan to be followed. Authentic technique springs from thoughtlessness when all pre-arranged forms are absent from consciousness and when the intellect is surrendered.

Only when one is faithful in training for a number of years, laborious years, may one feel an insight into this kind of non-technique. It must also be understood that this 'thoughtlessness' I describe is not a debility of the mind. Instead, it belongs to *Thien-ly*, the natural way, the way of Heaven."

Still a bit confused, but excited nonetheless, Xuan reported both his father's tale and his father's comments to Master Lam as the Master was instructing Xuan and a group of his fellow students.

The Master said, "Your father is absolutely correct. If during combat a combatant's mind flows toward a concern with a device, or to a stratagem to use, or toward a thought of defeating the opponent or a fear of being defeated, then that combatant is destined for defeat. This state of mind-flow results from one's continuing to rely on techniques that are born out of patterns of physical activity. Such patterns are embedded in the world of the ego-centered senses."

The Master said to the group, "Think now about Father Hau's story about the man of technique and the man of mind. As you can imagine, the man of technique still thought of himself as 'I' and his opponent as 'he.' His reasoning faculties were confined to the world of subjectivity and objectivity. In this dualistic consciousness, he could not merge with the cosmic forces that enable one to transcend consciousness. The man of technique had not yet moved beyond that ego-centered state. He was unable to identify with the cosmos. It is evident that since the man of technique still relied on his physical skills, clung to them, thought about them, cherished them, he resided in the inferior position even before the actual combat began. Had he been able to go against the grain of his conformity with technique, his skill might have served him for a while.

"But technique, however refined, is superficial. The man of the school of technique lacked the training and development of his mental and spiritual processes, which are the essence of martial art. As the man of technique had been defeated in the pugilistic contest that morning, and as he lacked the ability to separate the defeat and his ego, his thoughts continued to be occupied with winning and losing.

"In this agitated state of mind, facing an opponent whose attitude and mind were obviously composed and who revealed no fear whatsoever, the man of technique was finished. His opponent's perfect equanimity evoked a domination which, of itself, forced submission.

"As you yourself learned when you were a beginner in martial arts," continued Master Lam, "technical contrivances are important in the early stages of learning the art, but mental and spiritual elements are the *sine qua non*. The mental and spiritual follow the natural course of the divinely ordained cosmos.

"The layman does not consider, and certainly does not comprehend this phenomenon, for it is largely indescribable and therefore inexplicable. As we may try to explain it, it retreats from our comprehension, for its origin is beyond ordinary human consciousness, and its process is profoundly mysterious. It is not from another place but it is of another dimension. The phenomenon of which I speak is 'Cosmic *Yi*,' and one may only begin to comprehend its profound meaning by exploring awareness based on experiencing it."

"Master," inquired a student, "wouldn't the world be vastly improved if everyone were taught these truths?"

"Yes, assuredly," replied the Master. "But it is probably a total waste of time trying to explain it to laypersons, for as we can see from witnessing the behavior of our own townspeople, they are interested in martial arts only as swordplay and bone-breaking, not as models of forbearance, discipline, and restraint.

"As for your father's example, Xuan, when the practitioner of the *Yi* school, the school of mind, reached a certain spiritual state, that spirit unfolded so overwhelmingly that no fighting was needed, and the opponent simply recognized defeat. The man of *Yi* defeated his technically proficient opponent before physical combat began. His opponent, not being physically injured by any attack but profoundly humiliated, felt that he wanted to die honorably by his own hand. Nowadays we are puzzled by the thought of someone choosing to end his own life as a result of a defeat at arms, but historians assure us that seeking rectitude by this means was until recent times considered a martial virtue."

The Master thought a moment before proceeding. "I hope you all remember that the story Xuan's father Hau related does indeed distinguish two very different schools of thought about martial art. The first believes that whenever the goals of the *Yi* training have been achieved, the practitioner will be effective in combat, no matter whether weapons or empty-hand methods are employed.

"The second school asserts that effectiveness in combat must be based on technique, and that technical ability is enough. Of course, that second way of looking at martial art effectiveness is the simple-minded, childish view, the belief of the masses, of our townsfolk. The second view is the equivalent of 'common sense.'

"'Ah!' you will say, 'common sense.' But that is good. However, I would remind you that 'common sense' is that technique which reveals to us that the world is flat. In martial arts, the reality is different. The followers of the technical schools that concentrate on technical skills may obtain rapid progress. Students of those schools may surpass in practical applications all their counterparts in other schools—for the first five years. But if the training is continued for ten years, the two schools become comparable. And beyond ten years, the *Yi* schools, the schools of mind—or I should say 'mindfulness,'—begin to prove stronger and their technical ability becomes more effective. After twenty years of training, followers of *Yi* schools will leave their technical opponents far, far behind.

"Keep always in mind that combatants are dynamic, whereas techniques are static. Combatants use the techniques; the techniques do not use the combatants. Similarly, man is a vital entity, whereas weapons are inanimate. Humans must never allow themselves to be shackled by the static elements of weaponry. Techniques are external things; they can be learned from imitating, from showing. Mind, spirit are internal. They cannot be taught by words and languages, because words and languages contort meaning.

"As practitioners, you cannot rule out either the mental and spiritual training or the technical aspect. Technique without spirit is naive and dangerous. In combat, spirit without technique is useless. Both technique and spirit become part of our indivisible one in order for us to understand the essence of martial arts—and the purpose of martial arts training. Now, contemplate this parable of Chuang Tsu:

Emperor Hsuan of China was interested in cock fighting. He asked Chi Hsing Tsu, a famous trainer of fighting cocks to train a good one for him. When the season for cock fighting approached, the Emperor summoned Chi Hsing Tsu. "Is the cock ready?" he inquired.

Chi responded, "Not ready, Your Imperial Majesty. He is still full of rage." The Emperor was confused, for he believed that if the cock were full of rage, that rage was precisely the state of emotional readiness necessary for effective combat. Evidently Chi Hsing Tsu did not believe so, and the Emperor held his peace.

Ten days went by, and the Emperor was eager to know about the cock. He asked Chi again, and Chi's answer again was, "The cock is not yet ready, Sir. He still flares up whenever he sees another cock pass by. He becomes furious even when he hears the crowing of the other cocks at a distance." The Emperor was confused, for he was under the impression that if the cock flared up in rage, then he should be ready for combat. But evidently Chi Hsing Tsu did not believe so, and the Emperor held his peace.

Another ten days passed, and again Chi came at the Emperor's summons and responded to the Emperor's inquiry, "The cock is not quite ready, Sir. He still ruffles his feathers, although his hot-headed attitude has markedly diminished." The Emperor was growing impatient, but he bided his time.

Ten days later, the Emperor again summoned Chi for news of the cock's condition. "He is just about ready, Sir. He now resembles a wooden cock, still and empty. He shows no sign of readiness for combat, no apparent reaction of any kind, but when he roams about the yard, no other cock dares to appear in his presence. All run from him."

Finally, when Chi declared the cock ready for battle, and the Emperor presented the cock in combat, the opposing cocks ran away each time. The Emperor's cock defeated all in this manner. The Emperor was delighted but puzzled. "How is it, Chi, that this cock was not ready when he was in a rage, and then defeated all challengers when he seemingly had lost all his spirit?"

Chi Hsing Tsu responded, "Your Imperial Majesty, when first the cock manifested rage, I knew that such behavior signifies a lack of self-confidence and that the cock would respond in a different way to every challenger. But as he was freed from excitement the cock demonstrated increasing maturity. Finally, his supreme composure frightened his opponents, though he used no technical contrivance of any kind. His vigor of spirit overawed his opponents, and no combat was needed. He was a mature creature."

"This is a marvelous lesson for us all, Chi," said the Emperor, who at once made Chi chamberlain of the court.

"Of course Chi Hsing Tsu was not at all an ordinary trainer of cocks. Chi, a master of Tao, converted a cock, furious and full of rage into a peaceful creature. Now, I ask you, if a chicken can be trained to reach that high level, can a human?" Master Lam smiled, but only with his lips. Any of his students would have known from his expression that he was being ironic.

"So," concluded Master Lam, "as you now know, my young friends, the very beginning steps in the martial arts involve the learning of fighting techniques. To know how to fight is the preliminary step. To know how *not* to fight is to know the end. When one has integrated virtue into one's way of life, no fighting is necessary.

If someone were to say to you that in order to conquer an opponent, you need no technique or physical force, you might still question that statement.

"If someone were to ask you to listen to him with your heart, not with your ears, and tell you that you then will understand him better, you might still argue that God creates ears for hearing and listening, not the heart.

"If someone were to say to you that if you close your

eyes you will see better, more clearly, you might still argue that when one closes the eyes one becomes as the blind, for how can one see things with closed eyes?

"Your reasoning is absolutely relevant to the world around you. It is most rational. But such a quality of reason is fit only to serve your present capacity of understanding. And I must tell you that such a capacity is, perhaps like the cock's, immature and undeveloped.

"The mature mind, on the other hand, listens but does not always interpret. It listens to words but only to grasp their intention. The mature mind does not focus on the denotation of words, but on connotation. The mature mind listens in silence, and only in silence does it bloom."

Master Lam paused briefly and concluded, "Perhaps today's subject is beyond your capacity to comprehend it. It is too abstract, obtuse, not rational to your mind. However, there is much to think about in this irrational subject, and I must come back to you when the time is right. Yes, when the time is right."

With eyes wide open, Xuan and his fellow students stared at each other in confusion. They had now reached that very point of confusion for which the Master had hoped and aimed, for, as he reminded himself as he retired to his room, without confusion there can be no growth.

# 4

## A Way
## to the Unknown

Master Lam's reputation spread far and wide though, as usual, he lived a simple and tranquil life. Years ago, during his novitiate under Master Tai-Anh, there had been many other students besides Hau who were competent in fighting skills. One of them, Famho, was expelled from the school. Famho was also one who was singularly jealous of Lam's ability.

Now, even after twenty years had passed, Famho's envy was so sustained that he was still plotting ways to destroy Master Lam's influence among students and the population in general.

One morning as Master Lam led his students to the woods in search of medicinal plants for a herbal study, a dozen men leaped from the thicket and attacked the students. The students at once recognized their attackers as members of Famho's gang. Facing the sudden assault Master Lam stopped in his tracks, composed himself, and used the occasion as an opportunity to examine the fighting skills of his students under "field conditions." This was the first time Master Lam's students had had such an opportunity.

Master Lam maintained his calm demeanor for a few minutes, enough to acquire a "take" on each of his students. Then he pounced upon the attackers himself, but "pounced" in a very eccentric way—a manner of engagement that puzzled not only members of Famho's gang, but Lam's students as well.

For at first Master Lam staggered about, appearing to be ready to fall down at any moment, but soon he altered the aspects of his wobbling body, first defending and then attacking. His strange movements dazzled his opponents who were lured into thinking that he had jumped to the left when he had actually shifted to the right. Master Lam seemed to be about to attack from the front when he had already slipped to a gang member's rear. Using the drunkard-style of fighting with deceptive ease, Master Lam soon drove the ruffians away with noses bleeding and their joints and various organs in considerable pain.

The experience in the woods not only gave Master Lam a splendid opportunity to gauge the progress of his students, it also provided the students with a rare occasion to witness their Master in actual combat. After the students had rested, Master Lam said, "Let us continue our search for plants."

All then resumed the search, but in the minds of each

student remained great admiration for their Master's skill and spirit. One of the students raised the question, "Master, as you were defending us this morning, we did not recognize your using any single technique you have taught us. We wonder about this."

"Nonsense! You have been taught all of those techniques," responded the Master bluntly.

The students looked at each other, knitted their brows and said, "But Master, really, we have not seen those techniques before—not even one of them."

The Master seemed to change his mind. "Of course, you haven't seen *those techniques* before. You will never see them, at least by themselves. If you could recognize them as discrete 'moves,'—and you attempted to engage in combat using them— then your technique would be childish and derivative. That kind of 'monkey-see, monkey-do' is pure mediocrity. It is reserved for novices. But I have higher hopes for you. So let us continue the search for our herbs. We will return to this subject of recognizing 'moves' some time later." This order dampened the students' enthusiasm.

After two long hours of picking leaves or roots, flowers or berries of a number of plants, Master Lam and the students returned to the school, washed their harvest, and set the products in the sun to dry for the next herbal lesson.

During lunch that day, the students reminded the Master of the question that had puzzled them in the woods and that the Master had left unanswered. Master Lam hesitated briefly before answering, knowing that his explanation would be difficult, perhaps too difficult for his young students to assimilate.

"All right," he said. "You claim you had never before seen the techniques I executed this morning. In a way you are right, for I myself do not know what those techniques were—so how could you? On the other hand, Although I don't remember what my movements were, I know that the techniques I employed this morning were only variations on the basic ones with which you are all familiar.

"I merely adapted myself to circumstances unconsciously. I could not possibly conform my actions to some fixed 'routine'—any more than I would count the number of steps I was taking while running in a foot race. In other words, I could not use my conscious mind trying to remember any techniques during the combat." Master Lam posed as if he were about to defend against an attacker; he looked puzzled, stroked his chin. "Hm," he said, more or less to himself, "shall I use *nikkyo* on this fellow now? Or should I try *kote gaeshi* first?" Master Lam rolled his eyes and put his finger in his mouth, as would a puzzled child, and his students laughed at the sight of a perplexed Master-child planning how to respond to attack. "No, one does not think and plan during defense and attack. One alters the basic techniques one has learned, alters them without thinking and in accordance with necessity." The Master thought for a moment and smiled. "I did see some of you 'forget technique' this morning, but you were not aware of your responses then. That is good. That is excellent. That is another dimension of the training: to pass out of the sphere of the recognizable."

"Master, how do we enable ourselves to get out of the sphere of recognizable at will?" asked one student.

The Master smiled, "Perhaps you are asking, 'How do we know when we are authentically 'artistic?' Alas, authentic technique is within the realm of the unknowable. In order to move into that realm, one must lose one's mind and be defiled no longer by any dualistic concept, such as 'self' and 'opponent,' 'subject and object;' those pairs of opposites you must learn to dissolve into units of one. And then will appear the radiant, the ungraspable, the unpredictable. This appearance is the *void* which lies within the *unknown*, for the *known* is a product of thought, not reality."

"Well then, Master," persisted the student, "If the unknown is *void*, which means non-existent, formless, empty, then how can one grasp the techniques?"

"Ah," said the Master, "That is why I said it is ungraspable."

The student frowned, rolled his eyes, and sighed a great sigh.

"Yet," continued the Master in a patient tone, "this ungraspableness is intrinsically dynamic, constantly in motion, and not remaining for two consecutive seconds the same. When you are able to differentiate the dead techniques from the live, only then can you gain insights into your training. With the senses, you can remember the names and understand the forms, but you remain unable to comprehend the mystery of those forms that have no form. Beyond the senses, however, nothing is lost in the *void*. Everything appears therein."

Master Lam continued: "Remember well that *known* techniques must, by definition, be dead techniques. They are names written on paper, stored in the conscious mind. But the techniques that appear by necessity out of our unconscious are nameless, alive, appear and disappear from moment to moment in myriad ways, figures, shapes, forms, and velocities according to situation and circumstance. Those appearances and disappearances arise out of the inner workings of higher, pure consciousness, consciousness of nothing—not from one's ordinary consciousness of being and things.

"The mind is capable of moving from one *known* technique to other *known* techniques. But unfettered consciousness—superconsciousness—can range from the *known* to the *unknown*, laboring in ways the ordinary creative mind cannot approach. When the superconsciousness manifests itself, it dissolves into formlessness and the void. Nothing more can be said about this state, formlessness, for thoughtlessness is its nature.

"Forms? Forget them all, if you would reach the higher levels of training. Attach yourselves no longer to winning, losing, rank, grade. Such things are superficial, transitory, mere adornment which remain as barriers to higher learning. Remember always that techniques that can be described as 'terminology' are dead. Rank and grade are superficial adornment of the physical, and are meaningful only to neophytes.

"Again I say: the authentic, the true, the live techniques are unknowable."

"But, Master, if that is so," responded one student with a worried expression, "then every teacher teaches useless techniques. Then every teacher is guilty of great wrongs. What then of the teacher's professional conscience?"

The Master replied: "Guilty of 'great wrongs?' No, not at all. These superficial techniques, these beginnings do interest people. The teacher must employ them much as the conductor of an orchestra must tune up the instruments before the music can be enjoyed. The audience, you see, are already fascinated with the sound they expect to hear! So the conductor might say, 'This part is only the tuning up of our instruments, not the concert itself, so please restrain your enthusiasm!'

"Now, after the instruments have been given their basic tuning, their readiness, the conductor can lead the musicians into another level of performance, wherein the quintessence, the heart of the music can be approached and the interplay of melody and harmony revealed in all its purity.

"How irritating it is to see that the quintessence of art, its simplicity, is so often unattractive to the ordinary mind. It is also irritating but entirely necessary to begin teaching with showy techniques that, while appealing to the ignorant, have no substance and practicality.

"Real techniques—the unknowable, the ungraspable—reach us only when all knowable technique has been cleansed from the mind. Consider this example:

"A thief once made forced entry into the home of a wealthy family. His presence was discovered in the early morning hours by several servants who surrounded the intruder and held him at bay. The servants had brought staffs and knives and swords, and at first light sought to capture the thief.

"The master of the house appeared and the servants, trying to impress their employer, did their best to get close to the intruder and disable him. Although they tried and tried, they did not wish to risk injury to themselves, and so they made no progress.

"After an hour or so of this fruitless endeavor, an old man appeared and said, 'May I provide some assistance?'

"Out of general respect for the elderly the well-taught servants did not dismiss him outright, but they paid the old fellow almost no heed, for he appeared quite decrepit and anyway had no weapons. However, since they themselves were making no progress, they let the old man enter the hall where the thief was cornered.

"A short while later, the thief came staggering out of the hall, looking like a wrung-out towel. Nevertheless, all were certain that the thief had killed or incapacitated the old man. But hardly had they expressed that thought when the old man appeared at the door, erect and lively. The old man suggested that now that the thief had been defeated, and thus humiliated, he had been punished enough and should be left alone. All were astonished, for the old man said nothing else and departed.

"Had they been in the hall when the old man first entered they would have witnessed the thief suddenly cower in terror, as if frozen or bewitched. They would have seen the old man walk up to the thief, gently hit on certain vital points on the thief's arm, and order him to leave the house. Those gentle blows were vital and immediately effective enough to render the thief's body almost paralyzed. One might well believe that the thief's foul profession was ended at that moment and that he may have sought a better way of life thereafter.

"You have discerned already that the old man was a true expert in martial arts. His ability had reached such a degree that no physical effort was required to subdue his opponent. In fact, he needed to employ no fancy technique whatsoever. A mental phenomenon was sufficient for him to fulfill his task."

"Master, something was hidden there? Some secret advantage in the old man was hidden?"

Master Lam responded, "My master, Tai Anh, revealed to me that the old man's power belongs to the domain of *psychic training*. It is an activity growing out of the functional unconscious. And the old man had reached a high level in the practice *diem mat*, an art of hitting certain vital points so as to numb or immobilize.

"You may ask why the old man left so precipitously. Well, this, too, is in concert with the moral code of martial arts. Having successfully served others, the authentic practitioner expects neither compliment nor reward. He puts aside his self, gives up the desire for fame, name, gain. He becomes a person of Tao, an authentic master of *do*.

"Perhaps in rendering the thief incapable of further physical mischief, the old man performed an act of high morality. How, you say? Consider: He freed the thief and enabled that miserable fellow to convert himself into a new person.

"Beyond that, it is likely that the old man entered the state of *Te* (wisdom), the condition of having the power of discerning and judging timely and properly that which is the right and true way to perform a deed. For wisdom is the point for which one must aim beyond morality. Morality is only the preliminary state, a means to an end, not an end in itself.

"Wisdom is achieved only when one is able to give up violence, ill-will, hatred, and selfish desire. Using himself for the benefit of others, the old man was truly a model of the gentle master, for not only were his actions admirable, they were exemplary for all martial adepts.

"As for the actions of the thief, who knows what might have motivated his life of crime? Whatever its source, the criminal is a product of a disease of the age, an epidemic of our time. And such disease cannot be eliminated overnight, but may require generations to overcome. And to cure the diseases, one must address not only the diseases, but also the causes."

"Master," inquired a student, "you say 'one' must. Who might this 'one' be?"

"All of us, of course, are part of this 'one,' but among

us are those who volunteer or are elected or appointed to serve the public good. We refer to these people as 'authorities,' and we include among them teachers, legislators, police, judges, mayors, council members, and the like. We look to authorities for leadership and for vital example. When leaders exemplify right living and right action, then the people begin to feel a mysterious, positive, constructive energy in the society. The people are themselves then moved to right living and right action, and not only the symptoms of the 'disease,' but also the causes, begin to disappear.

"We have not seen this happen yet, but there are legends and tales of societies in which the people became virtuous. And the strange part of it, strange to most people, is that right thinking and right living requires no effort, only a giving up of greed and selfishness."

"Master, does not giving up greed and selfishness require effort, an effort of will, much like the effort of diligent and faithful training?"

"Well, yes, it is so," replied Master Lam. "One must pass through that stage, for it is part of the beginning. At that time, in the training, for example, your mind tells you 'relax, relax,' and you are not relaxed. Your mind is too busy thinking how to do this or that and your body becomes stiff. The very effort to make you 'relax' confines and hampers the natural flow of your energy. Therefore, make no effort. If you enjoy training, just train, and train faithfully, diligently. And when your training has reached a certain level, and when I see the time is right, I will shout at you: Drop that effort completely. Cling to that effort no longer, but simply train. And I am shouting at you now."

The Master looked at his students and asked, "What's the matter? Are you confused?"

"Yes, Master. It is really confusing, really confusing!"

"Good! But that very confusion is the point, the key to effortlessness. You will miss the point if you continue to strive. You will fail because your ego has swollen too much. Remember, if you are not empty, the *unknown* cannot enter.

"Experience shows us the way. If you will simply train, one day the conscious thought which guides your training will suddenly disappear together with that diligent and faithful effort. Your movements will become fluid. Your technique will become manifest without your effort; you will be filled with wonder and delight. Your art becomes artless, form becomes formless.

"On a higher plane yet, one might say that the art of artlessness is the art, and art for art's sake is not the art, for being is actually non-being and non-being is being.

"What do you mean, Master?" asked several students.

"I will also say that on this level, right is wrong and wrong is right, good is evil and evil is good, success is failure and failure is success. So saying, I do not mean that I encourage you to do wrong because I have said that wrong is right. For it is not possible to make such an assertion, standing on one side and opposing the other. Why is this?"

"Yes, yes, why is this, Master?" asked the students.

"One cannot choose one side and reject the other

because nothing in life is completely right and without wrong. So I say to you, do not choose. Do not choose. Do not even choose to not-choose. Only when you are beyond choosing can you reach the whole, the truth. Remember that effortlessness comes only after much effort, but one can never reach effortlessness by any other means, for as you must know by now, the faster one hurries, the slower one reaches. "Consider this:

A man once wrote a book, and his publisher requested an illustration for the book, a Chinese ideograph, in calligraphy. Just one character.

"The man first practiced writing this character, again and again, concentrating on every stroke of the brush. When he had used almost nine hundred sheets of paper in his quest he was still dissatisfied with the result. As he was distracted by something else, he idly picked up one more sheet, inked his brush and, without thinking about what he was doing, created another ideograph. Suddenly he looked at the page, as if seeing it for the first time. He had created the best calligraphy in his experience. It exemplified gracefulness, simplicity, vigor, and generosity of spirit. It would be an imposing creation in the eyes of any calligrapher.

"The man later said that he accomplished his beautiful work effortlessly, thoughtlessly. It was as if he had been occupied by something from *beyond the known*, for an unknown force manifested itself. We may say that the man experienced a state of unconsciousness in which a total emptiness prevailed.

"From that account I realized that whenever the mind becomes unconscious of itself, of its working, the state of egolessness may appear and its wonders occur. But I have said this before, have I not? My throat is parched, my voice has become husky because of talking many times about this same thing, but none of you seem to weigh my words seriously. Sometimes I think I am talking to the wall."

"We are trying," said several of the students at once, "We are trying, Master!"

The Master sighed and began his conclusion of the lesson. "Some of you have practiced different styles. Some of you have relished seminars held here and there. And I say, it is quite all right for you to experience diverse prospects. You may acquire some special good feelings and accumulate some extra know-how. But remember my words: Don't be lost in those phantasmagoria. Don't be misled by superficial phenomena, for they are nothing. They are merely different forms. And now you understand that real techniques are formless.

"So, meditate on this situation. Look inside and you will perhaps become more in harmony with the inner darkness, and from there you may be able to see more of the whole. Once you witness that whole, you will bloom like a flower, effortlessly.

"That flower does not bloom for people who call it forth. It blooms when the time comes for it to bloom. The flower does not advertise. It simply is, in all its beauty and fragrance.

"Once a master has witnessed the blooming, and has himself begun to bloom, he faces many unforeseen problems, for frequently his conduct, speech, or silences may alienate his students. They may believe him to have become eccentric, abnormal, weird. And the master who has begun the blooming smiles, for he knows that the minds of his critics are not developed to witness the blooming; they live within their own limited capacity and on their own plane. That master makes no effort to correct impressions others have of him. He simply blooms.

"Most of you have passed the neophyte's need for the games of rank, grade, garments, and so on. But you still cherish those games dearly and recall fondly your various triumphs that brought a new grade. Think now. Those very recollections create a barrier to your higher learning. It is time to say goodbye to those artifices and make way for a new vision, a new way of training.

"I do not suggest that you reject your teachers, masters, organization. I do not suggest that you eschew loyalty, gratitude, and respect for them. But you must move to live in a different time. You must not remain static, holding and cherishing the old ways. You must move with the changing times and grow together, grow peacefully together.

"Wonders will bloom. Trust me."

# 5

# THE LIGHT OF DUSK AND THE LIGHT OF DAWN

THE HOMELAND had undergone great calamity and turmoil, the outcome of an obscene contest of ideologies that pitted North against South, brother against brother. The South succumbed to the North, and the fear of the new unknown regime caused thousands of people to seek to flee their country in panic. In that frenzy Hau, who had been seriously disabled in battle, gathered his family and fled to a totally alien, far, new land.

Like thousands of other refugees, Hau encountered great difficulties in the new land. He could not avoid the multifold shocks the new land presented at every turn, but he endured these travails, feeling compelled to accept everything in his new life. One of Hau's most ardent wishes was to acquire a good formal education for his son, Xuan.

Hau's concept of education was ingrained in his

martial arts orientation—a traditional view. The purpose of education was not only to train people for a career and a secure job, but to provide examples and qualities to help one live a worthwhile life in society. An effective education, Hau believed, must help one learn sharing, loving-kindness, compassion.

After some months, Hau began to believe that his fellow refugees in the new land were slipping away from prizing these qualities. It seemed to him that all his fellows now talked about and cared about were acquiring large salaries, expensive houses, luxury automobiles, fame, power, prestige, and the like. They seemed to have lost an inner compass that might enable them to examine their own conduct and direction.

Offended by the gross consumerism he witnessed, worried about Xuan's future, surrounded as Xuan was by these corrosive elements and as yet incomplete in his martial arts training, Hau sighed sorrowfully. He thought to himself, "How many really know how to live a meaningful inner life? I must find a supplement for Xuan's education." Because Xuan had become a young man under the tutelage of Master Lam, Hau believed that Xuan must continue in martial arts, but now the question was how to find the right master?

In their search for an authentic master in the new land, Hau and Xuan encountered one disappointment after another. They did find teachers who were glamorous in appearance and offered rank and grade rapidly, with instruction in all kinds of weapons and techniques, and certificates and public recognition to go with everything. They found teachers who concentrated on punching and kicking. They found teachers whose marketing of martial arts equipment and clothing seemed to be their chief talent. They found teachers who sought to have their students quickly engage in tournaments and strive to win trophies for fighting. They found that in each of these teachers certain vital qualities were missing.

Young Xuan had experienced years of training under an authentic master, but he now discovered in the new land that the martial arts teachers with whom he came in contact seemed to him not to possess an adequate teaching qualification—not only in terms of technique, but ethics.

Although he lived a relatively secure life among his family, Xuan was not at ease. He was now nearly twenty-one, in his last year of college, a young man full of vigor and ambition. But he was disheartened. What Master Lam taught, and *how* Master Lam taught seemed lost to Xuan forever. Martial arts in the new land was suffocating, he felt, not liberating. Although he had a firm foundation in martial arts basics, Xuan felt sorry for the beginners there. The martial arts atmosphere was unhealthy for them. Xuan felt at an impasse, unable to make a move in the direction he thought appropriate.

But each time Xuan became distressed, Master Lam appeared in his mind, pointing at him and saying: "You must believe in yourself. You must rely on your integrity and your strength, and then a bright moment will come. Time will change things. Have patience. Perseverance is the key." And then Xuan recovered his balance and felt better at once.

A thought flashed through Xuan's mind. He recalled a memory of his classmate Totu, when both he and Totu were twelve years old. Xuan wondered whether Totu was still alive and whether he, too, was drifting in this foreign land to which some of the people had migrated after the war. He did not know. But to Xuan, Totu was an unforgettable friend. For Xuan remembered how one day after an unusual training session, Totu had suddenly saddened and wept.

When a senior member asked: "In the past when the Master hit you hard you never cried. Why the tears today?"

Totu turned his head away. Questioned again, he said, "He hit hard today, too, but I did not feel any pain. That is why I weep. Do you understand?"

That answer with its subtle underlying reason revealed the deep love Totu held for the Master, a regard with its own beauty that nowadays is difficult to find among the ranks of students, even the mature ones.

In that mood of recollection, Xuan associated another memory that made it impossible for him ever to forget Totu.

One day Xuan witnessed Totu greeting a young man of about twenty who had come to join the school. Totu asked the visitor if he carried an introductory letter, but the visitor did not respond. Instead, he looked around the hall and said, "How come I don't see any trophies or awards around your school?"

Totu honestly replied, "We don't fight in tournaments and so we don't collect trophies and awards."

Astonished by the answer, the visitor asked again, "Well, why don't you go and 'mix it up' so you can exhibit the superiority of your system, your power, your art?"

Recognizing that the visitor's entire attitude did not conform with the objectives of the school, Totu said, "We don't fight to win over others, but we do have so many rewards we don't even know how to display them."

"You don't fight to win over others and yet you have many rewards? Your rewards are invisible then? I guess they're imaginary, eh?" The visitor laughed, but then frowned. "Are you making fun of me?" The visitor's face had become quite red.

"You might say so," bluntly replied Totu.

And at that the visitor directed a punch at Totu's face followed by a round-house kick, after which he fell suddenly to the floor, looking surprised and pained, for he keenly felt but had not even seen Totu's rapid physical response.

But the visitor did hear all of Totu's spoken response. "Sorry for your inconvenience," Totu said as he walked away. "What you just received was part of our 'invisible visible' reward."

These two memories of Totu helped firm Xuan's respect and admiration for his friend.

One autumn morning in the new land, looking out into the courtyard of his family home where multicolored flowers fell and covered the ground, Xuan suddenly recalled the many mornings that he and Totu and their fellow students swept the ground before the day's lessons began. But now those classmates were no longer there, and he would never again train with them or see the trees with their flamboyant fall colors and the radiant flowers in the courtyard of the Master's school. Feeling suddenly ill and overcome by emotion, Xuan was prompted to write a letter to Master Lam:

My Dear Master,

It has been a long time since I have written to you, Master. I deserve to be reprimanded and punished. Please forgive me for my idleness in this regard.

I have encountered many challenges since I came to this new country, struggling day in, day out, trying to construct a new life. In spite of difficulties, my heart is always with you and the school. I pray that you may have perfect health.

I have been away from home for four years now. I really miss you and my classmates, and my training. Your kind of lessons in chivalry, honesty, humanness, faithfulness, loyalty in martial arts are hard to find here, Master. I do carry those qualities in my heart, and I have been doing my best at every turn. But one major problem that has upset me for some time is that the more I try to exercise those qualities here, the more I am misunderstood and ridiculed.

Whereas you have always encouraged us to seek the voice of our hearts, the teachers here favor and promote only those who follow them like a flock of sheep. The teachers thus create factions and focus their attention on acquiring more partisans. These teachers keep preaching "harmony," but they create conflict; they preach "love," but they sow the seeds of rivalry, even enmity; they speak of the Oneness of all beings, but they expend great effort to maintain their personal superiority. I see not one action of harmony or love from them, but only egoistic and prejudicial practices. I have heard and witnessed people complaining about these injustices, but I have also become a victim myself.

In the *dojos* I have visited, I am unable to act freely according to my conscience. Such behavior is not allowed. One is required to "follow directions." I realize I am living now in a very different martial arts world, a world in which those who are in control always claim to be right, and are accepted as right, no matter what. I am keenly aware that I am different from my fellow students, and I feel thus oppressed.

Master, I strive in all I do to exemplify virtue, but my virtue is often thrust back in my face. I then must ask myself if this world is so constituted that it is the honest and the virtuous who are subject to unjust criticism and treatment. I only wish for a bit more sympathy, righteousness, and understanding in the world. Then human society might become more harmonious and peaceful.

Regrettably, there is less here of those qualities— rather than more. The concern of the people is with the head rather than with the heart. I have come to the conclusion that as our people become more "civilized" to the so-called First World, the less are their hearts trained, because heart-training does not "pay off," whereas head-training does.

A teacher here once told me, "You don't get what you deserve, Sonny, you get what you negotiate." Love, art, faith, truth, are they all subject to negotiation? It puzzled me for some time, until I awakened to the reality that I am also now living in a mad world.

What pains me most of all, dear Master, and disheartens me most of all, is that I can see clearly now that Asian martial arts in the Western world have been pointed in a new direction. That new direction surely leads to decadence, especially on the spiritual level where ethics and morality seem totally missing in the instruction, in the attitudes, and in the practices. The very ground has been destroyed.

Though the growth and expansion of martial arts here are remarkable, and though all around me are rejoicing in its bright light, yet this light is comparable only with a twilight. And the more I look into the heart of the situation, the better I come to understand the true meaning of the martial arts discipline you teach and the reasons why people in the homeland, and in the East generally, venerate and consider it with respect and reverence.

Master, I remember so well the day I was introduced to you by my father. I remember that on the very first day you said you would make me a man, a real human being. I was so immature I could not understand what you meant by "real man." But for the eight years I grew under your benevolent tutelage, I gradually absorbed its intent and the real meaning of "real human being."

Before I left home, you advised me to enroll in any school of martial arts in the new land, or study any system I felt like. You also instructed me again and again that what I train is not important; the real importance is how I train. These instructions are firmly engraved in my heart, and I have done as you said.

But, Master, the way they train here is diametrically opposed to your method. They stress the physical. They worship technical prowess rather than the development and well-being of the students. I can see that there are many, many errors in this way of teaching, and I cannot bear it.

I must confess to you, Master, that I have revolted against the martial arts organization I joined here. I confess to bearing a grudge against them, but that grudge is valid and necessary, I think.

Some of my fellow students and I comprise a group of people of varied ethnic backgrounds who share the same feeling of displeasure. We have found nothing in the leadership that deserves praise. The whole directorship of the organization to which we belong appears day by day so prejudiced, partial, and cruel that the loyalty of its members is crushed. In the long run it is the very edifice of the martial arts that is destroyed. I feel pity for my colleagues to be trapped in such a dreary and disgraceful situation.

We see even "learned people" drawn by the offered bubble of reputation, rank, and grade falling one after another into the same shameful ditch. I wonder how the more innocent and naive followers can possibly be spared from the same fate.

Once in a while people have tackled the true path of training, but the subject was quickly dropped and never picked up again. The main part of authentic training has simply slipped by.

I have wondered and wondered how those teachers could continue to miss the point, and I easily come to the conclusion that they must not be the mirrors that we should try to emulate. They truly say 'do as I say, not as I do.'

I remember you said that the study of the path—the *do*—is the path of inner change, and that only when one can move to the inner path can one be transformed. I am disappointed to see that the majority of my Western colleagues ignore the true meaning of the *do*. Of course, most of them have never been even exposed to the concept.

I sometimes ask myself: "Should those who have assumed leadership of martial arts here, with the society in such turmoil and the youth so rootless, wandering, and uncontrolled, and the streets so dangerous and the elders so fearful, now try to identify and agree upon important values to teach and establish? Should they now try to restructure some of the ways they teach martial arts so as to emphasize those values instead of continuing to concentrate on empty surface tricks?"

But it seems more and more likely that they are simply not aware of what they are actually doing; not aware of the real outcomes of their teachings; and not aware of the waste of time and effort their approach to martial arts really is.

They *are* aware that their martial arts enterprises are economic, commercial, and entertainment successes, and that they are in control. They will brook no opposition to that control. And of course if economic, commercial, and entertainment success is all that counts, then they are "successful" and there is no reason for change! They must not see the shallow vulgarity of it. They must not be able to see that the enterprise they call "martial arts spirit" or *budo* is a gross perversion of those noble terms.

I saw an advertisement recently that encapsulates that perversion. "How to Make $100,000 a Year Teaching Martial Arts!" it proclaimed. It then went on to describe how to sell a "get your black belt program for $2,000 and collect the money 'up front.'" Not a word about character development, etc. Not a word!

Then, dear Master, I thought: "If I continue condemning others I shall close off the possibility of my own growth." So I have tried to stop blaming. Moreover, I remember you once said: "A single swallow does not make the spring," and "To know how to wait is the greatest preparation for accomplishment." I am exercising those qualities—waiting for more swallows to join in thought, to warm my lonely soul and to make a radiant spring. Perhaps I shall find yet a teacher of merit. Next week I shall travel to another city nearby and try to find your one-time student Henry Irving, of whom you spoke so highly. Perhaps Mr. Henry teaches in your spirit.

Dear Master, after all this, in reconsidering the falseness and hypocrisy of life as most people seem to live it, I have finally come to a definite resolution: I shall accept everything. I shall not reject anything, but with perfect calmness I shall allow everything to happen. I bear no grudge toward anyone or anything. I am for everything because, as you once said, everything can be used to reach its opposite. "By suffering without complaint, you shall know the truth of life. You must believe in yourself, rely on your integrity, and your strength, and when these conditions are fully matured, the right moment will come by itself. Time will change everything." You used to say so, and I wish I were on the way.

Dear Master, excuse me for writing such a lengthy complaining letter, but I cannot pour out my inner feelings to anyone but you.

Your faithful disciple,
Xuan Le

# 6

# THE 'UNRESOLVABLE' PROBLEM

IN THE HOMELAND, Master Lam gazed upon his garden thinking about the fortunes of Hau Le and family, and especially about Hau's son, Xuan, Master Lam's favorite student now in a land far away. The letter from Xuan lay in his lap, creased and re-creased, for Master Lam had read the letter again and again, each time learning something new from Xuan's words—and also from what Xuan had not said.

Master Lam was surprised and happy to learn that Xuan would now try to make contact with Mr. Henry, a highly competent Westerner with a fine spirit. Henry had studied with Master Lam, and established a school of martial arts when he returned to his country.

Upon first reading the letter, Master Lam felt satisfaction, for whereas Xuan had complained of life's ups and downs, he had also said that at last he had come to an end of complaining. When Master Lam had read Xuan's letter aloud to his students, he had commented about that "end of complaining."

"This is a good sign," Master Lam said to the students. "Xuan says that he has ceased to dispute with others, and that's even better. For, you see, that cessation becomes a healing force which can help one cure the anxieties, anguishes, and worries—the vicissitudes of life—that one must experience to be able to call oneself human. Otherwise Xuan, without suffering, would have remained entangled in a dull, ordinary life. How beautiful that Xuan has realized that life is not following him, but that he must flow with life!" The Master nodded several times in satisfaction. "Xuan has grown," he said, and smiled. All the students were glad.

By now Master Lam had read the letter many times and had seen something that the written words did not say. He saw that Xuan was deeply depressed, possibly quite ill, and that the few words he wrote that sounded optimistic and inspiring, were likely but wishful thinking. "Something is working here that is not good," Master Lam sighed to himself. Xuan seemed to be suffering more than he revealed openly, and it was only Master Lam's insight that allowed him to receive the message.

Master Lam could see that Xuan was sinking slowly but surely, and deeply inside himself. He must not be allowed to construct an impenetrable shell that Master Lam had seen surrounding other sensitive people for whom life becomes too much.

Master Lam also knew that time often heals more

effectively than medicines, and that one such as Xuan, trained classically in the martial arts, may require a period to work out problems without intervention. Master Lam decided to wait for more word from Xuan.

He had several other thoughts at the moment that also tugged at his attention. One of these thoughts was of "The Vanquished," the blustery challenger who had lost in a trial of combat to Master Lam some time before and who had promised to return to Master Lam's school and serve him. The Vanquished had broken his word. He had not returned. Rumor from Master Lam's acquaintances in several cities seemed to point to The Vanquished's having fled the country.

This flight of The Vanquished pained Master Lam, not because he had lost a potential student, but because in fleeing, the obviously needful young man had made a bad choice, had stained his own honor, and had lost the opportunity to recover far more than his loss. "Well," thought Master Lam, "life has its hardships, perils, hindrances. One has to stumble against and over hard experiences to understand what life is about. After such experiences one may better be able to look at things with calmness, with all total consciousness available." But that The Vanquished would suffer, Master Lam was sure.

Master Lam was pleased when he heard that Xuan had encountered Henry Irving. Among the few foreigners who had studied with Master Lam, Mr. Henry had been the significant exception: the Westerner who could surrender at least part of himself to Master Lam's teaching methodology, and for whom it was conceivable that one day he might be able to master his ego. Master Lam had regretted Mr. Henry's departure from training, it was far too soon for the best effects to occur. Mr. Henry would benefit from having trained with Master Lam, but would be cut off from the kind of growth proceeding from an authentic education in martial arts.

The letter from Xuan's father that came soon after Xuan's letter invited Master Lam to visit Hau's family in the far land. Hau confirmed Master Lam's suspicion: Xuan was indeed gravely ill, and no physician could diagnose the sickness, and no cure seemed imminent. Xuan was becoming weaker every day, Hau revealed. He sometimes talked in his sleep and called out Master Lam's name. The letter, Master Lam saw, was more than an invitation. It was an appeal, and Master Lam decided to make the long journey over the sea.

Arriving in a new land, Master Lam was very much impressed by its grandiosity: imposing skyscrapers, long and broad highways crowded with all kinds of vehicles, with traffic moving along smoothly and rapidly, and without the constant clangor of automobile horns as in his homeland.

Master Lam nodded, acknowledging that Western technology had reached a very high degree of perfection. Soon his cab arrived at its destination, and greeted by his old friend Hau Le, Master Lam was touched and excited. He could see his joy reflected in the eyes of his friend.

Needless to say, the reunion of Master Lam and the

Le family was one of the most joyful moments of their lives. Master Lam was reunited with his most responsive, most promising student; Xuan, with the most influential person in his young life.

The minute he saw his Master, Xuan's listless expression became bright, alert, cheerful. He struggled to sit up but failed. He mumbled, "Forgive me, Master." Then, closing his sunken eyes in embarrassment, and too weak to continue, Xuan stretched out his lanky legs, his aspect resembling that of a dead person.

"There is no need for forgiveness, Xuan," said Master Lam. "Just turn this way and look at me and answer a few questions." And the Master then took Xuan's pulse and proceeded to engage in the interview common to the expert Asian healer. The interview consisted of a series of questions, the answers to which Master Lam listened with scrupulous attentiveness. Master Lam was concerned not only with Xuan's body, but also with his mind, his emotions, and his environment. Master Lam's method was holistic, empirical but not "logical," and not at all concerned with the functions of the body that might be compartmentalized and analyzed separately.

Following his examination, Master Lam concluded that Xuan's illness was due to a considerable fluctuation of mental and emotional states agitated by Xuan's prolonged anger and melancholy. Master Lam prescribed herbs to relieve Xuan's anorexia and to regulate the energy imbalance of Xuan's body. Master Lam prescribed a dramatic change in diet and planned ways to alter Xuan's emotional responses.

Twice during each of the following days Master Lam emitted his *ch'i* to various parts of Xuan's body, stimulating the main points to open certain stagnant channels of energy. Xuan began to feel a lukewarm current running throughout his body.

On the third day, Xuan admitted to feeling much more comfortable. He had already recovered some of his strength and was now sitting up, smiling cheerfully, eating rather heartily, and occasionally engaging in conversation.

After two weeks of Master Lam's attention—Xuan had regained much of his lost strength. At the end of four weeks the treatment became intermittent, Xuan had recovered his vigor, and had fully regained use of his legs.

Before Master Lam's arrival, and during the onset and early weeks of Xuan's illness, Henry Irving had called frequently as to Xuan's condition, and Hau had informed him that Master Lam would soon arrive. Henry was delighted at the prospect of seeing his old Master once again, and perhaps facilitating a meeting with him amd the other martial arts teachers who Henry believed were sincerely in search of authentic teaching. He organized a welcoming reception for Master Lam, and invited many martial arts teachers. Master Lam was pleased to learn of the reception plans and happily agreed to participate.

At the gathering were many well-known teachers and practitioners of a variety of martial disciplines, all persons native to the new land. Master Lam was greeted with great respect, for his reputation had preceded him by many years. The teachers felt honored to greet and meet him.

Several commented, however, that one of their number was not present and wondered what had kept him. This absent person was not native to the new land and had, they said, come from Master Lam's own country, establishing his own school in a city not far away. His name was "V."

Master Lam made no comment and registered no expression when the name of the absent teacher was pronounced, even though he recognized "V's" name as The Vanquished. Master Lam listened as the social conversation progressed and discovered that "V" was now the proprietor of a commercial *dojo*; that is, a martial arts school that advertised widely the rapid availability of "black belts" and other awards to those who were "fully paid-up members."

In this new land of opportunity, no one knew the history of The Vanquished in his native country. They did not know that he had never knelt before a Master, had never taken oaths of faithfulness and sincerity and subscribed to other virtues. They did not realize that The Vanquished had never suffered a lengthy period as a novice, had never learned the philosophy on which authentic martial arts rest. They knew only that the sturdy fellow seemed technically competent, that he was remarkably self-confident, and that he had proclaimed himself to be the suzerain of a secret system of combat passed on in his family from generation to generation.

The Vanquished was also known among the other teachers for boasting of his prowess. In other words, The Vanquished was considered by the other teachers to be something of a braggart and blowhard.

Upon discreet questioning by Master Lam, Henry disclosed that over time, The Vanquished's bluster and declarations of great power and claims of world-wide admiration and the continued self-promotion, had the effect of fascinating ignorant people who were searching for something dazzling and seemingly powerful that might, for a fee, rub off onto themselves. The Vanquished had discovered the psychology most effective in deceiving common folk. However, Henry remarked, the man's character flaws became only too evident after a while and students began to drop off, so that The Vanquished was unable to maintain success for long in any one city. The Vanquished found it necessary to move from place to place, each time beginning a new cycle of bluster and brag, profit and then loss.

It was to his credit that The Vanquished did not appear at the reception for Master Lam. Perhaps the main reason for his absence was shame for his failure to keep his word to Master Lam. The absence of The Vanquished was also a relief to Henry, who admitted to Master Lam that he felt obligated to invite the rude one simply because he was a martial arts teacher. Henry had hoped *all* martial arts teachers might profit from associating with Master Lam.

Several of the teachers commented discreetly at the reception about how simple and unassuming Master

Lam was. They found his humility remarkable and re-marked that such a celebrated master of the martial arts could have such a gentle and peaceful expression. All felt relaxed and at ease in the presence of Master Lam. After a time for Henry's welcoming remarks, general social greetings, and introductions, Master Lam suggested they all sit on the mat. He then welcomed any questions from the group.

"Master," said Larry, a senior teacher, obviously unburdening himself, "there are several questions that really bother most of us."

"I am happy for you," replied Master Lam, to the surprise of all. "You are bothered by several questions. I am bothered by many!" His face creased in a merry smile, and all the teachers laughed with him. He raised his hand and continued, "No! Not really. I make the joke, for questions are a sign of activity, of concern, of possible growth. I welcome questions!"

"Well," said the senior teacher, "the first trouble-some question is, since there are so many, which martial arts system is the true one? How can we ignorant souls recognize which system is mimicking the other? Most of us have been involved in the study for at least a decade or so, acquiring many different styles and many techniques, yet from what Henry has suggested to us we are still not on the proper way. Many of us feel that we may have reached nowhere. In the meantime our bodies have become older and weaker. What is the truth about the training? This is our great frustration."

"Ah, several questions there. Well, I shall do my best

to respond," said Master Lam with a small smile. All laughed. "All authentic systems share the same principle. It must be this way, since all are fighting arts. Therefore, there is no good system and no bad system—only good teacher and bad teacher, good student, bad student. Perhaps you asked, 'which system mimics the other?' And I must again respond, 'There is but one art: the art of fighting.' Whatever name you give it, that art still belongs to the art of fighting. And since there is but one art, the more one becomes near-perfect in one system, the more one's techniques appear to emulate the techniques at a very high level in another system."

"Do you mean to say that at the highest levels of skill the techniques of the various fighting disciplines appear to be the same?" asked Larry again.

"Exactly," said Master Lam. "At such a level, what appears to be mimicry is not mimicry, not imitation. Let me make another point. As you become more and more adept in a fighting art, you are likely to accumulate techniques from different styles." Master Lam paused and thought before he continued. "Well, I must except from that statement Western sports competitions, like Western pugilism and fencing, for they are limited by rigid rules of engagement. But for all the other martial arts very competent people often accumulate techniques from different styles. And you may enjoy practicing such a multiplicity of forms."

"Is that really an honorable course of action? To stray into another discipline?" another teacher, Casey, asked with a worried expression.

"That is alright. The external world seduces people with its attractiveness and its various lures. Only keep in mind that those techniques and forms that you come to love so much are not much use at your present status. That is, these sparkling techniques borrowed consciously from any art won't help much on your search for authenticity, for they are only appearance, and appearance cannot help you inside. Your being remains totally unaffected and you are then not much different from the monkey who sees and does." Master Lam smiled and looked about the group.

"Ah! 'Monkey-see, monkey-do!' is the way it is said, an expression I have only recently learned in your language. It is very apt for this situation." The teachers laughed appreciatively. "Monkeys are great imitators."

"Then do you mean that a borrowed technique is not 'all right' after all?" inquired Casey.

"I mean that something imitated is by definition not yours, not original, not sprung from your own being." Master Lam paused for emphasis. "Not authentic."

"Ah," said several teachers. "Hm," said others, thinking about the Master's words and the implication carried by those words. Others stared vacantly, the significance of the Master's words not connecting with their practice.

The Master allowed some time for his words to make their way toward understanding. Finally he spoke once again. "Please note that technique is only a means, a medium, a vehicle to carry some communications, some messages. Even if you can perform all kinds of techniques, and even if you can remember by heart all kinds of philosophies, it makes no difference, for they are not your own. You gain nothing spiritually from memorizing philosophies and learning a variety of new tricks. Your art becomes only physical exercise, game, entertainment."

There was a long silence in the hall. Master Lam gazed at the floor. The teachers looked at each other, some frowning, others shaking their heads. Several bowed wordlessly, arose, and left the hall. Alas, the truth is often cruel whether or not its expression is callous.

"But Master," said Owen, one of the number who stayed, "some of us have been training for thirty years. Aren't we supposed to know something? You're telling us that our kind of knowledge is not our own, and, is in fact, useless?"

The speaker was interrupted by the younger teacher Burt, "If not those techniques and philosophies we 'borrow' from somebody, from somewhere, then which one might we finally call our own?"

Another speaker, Gordon, interrupted the interrupter, "Or how does it become our own?" Gordon's facial expression was that of a person grieving a great loss. "Do we know nothing after all these years?"

In a very gentle voice and in a sympathetic tone the Master responded. "Of course you know something. You know many things. But those things do not lead you anywhere. Your energies go on moving, floating like clouds dissipating in the sky. Your body exists but is not alive. Your art exists but is not flowering. Your art is dead, like a dead body. You may decorate the dead body with rank and grade. You may honor the body with meritorious deeds. You may attire it with fancy clothing. You may put red on fingernails or on the lips, but all these are ornament. Decorations are useless in the martial arts."

More silence in the hall. Several others bowed, arose, and left. The Master sighed.

"My friends," said Master Lam to the remaining teachers, "after a certain phase of our training, somehow our 'knowledge' has to be transcended. That transcendence must be independent of our mind. The process remains unknown to us. Human knowledge cannot reach it. You may ask, how is this so? And I answer, because knowledge can arise only in the course of synthesizing the ideas of the senses. That is why our martial arts forefathers said, When there is no knowledge, knowing happens and reality appears.

"Real knowledge is self-knowledge. It requires a calm, clear, and empty mind, free from all kinds of distorted influences, like greed, fear, and so on. Instead, we must imbue every facet of our life with love, compassion, generosity, and wholehearted spirituality. Only then can truth be reflected and be perceived. This quality of consciousness arises where spirituality resides, beyond the limits of our senses. It is what you are actually looking and striving for, is it not?"

There was another silence. Then Henry spoke up in a quiet, intense voice. "Yes, yes, Master Lam. Yes! Spirituality is exactly what we are missing, what we are seeking. I'm ashamed to have to confess that we have spent our time and energy looking for something outside ourselves. We have been chasing power, wealth, fame. Isn't that true?" He looked at his colleagues for confirmation. A few nodded their heads.

"Here we've been, organizing workshop after workshop, seminar after seminar here and there, scheming to recruit more followers by putting-down other clubs and martial arts schools and promoting ourselves as the 'only way to go.' Frankly, I'm ashamed of myself." Henry looked down at the mat, his lips tight, as if he were about to weep.

Now Christiane, profoundly affected by Henry's remarks, spoke up, "People even betray their own Masters for selfish, immediate gain, forgetting their basic moral obligation. That despicable behavior happened right here in our own city." The others turned toward the speaker, nodding in agreement. "And money and sex have become the criteria in the lives of most of our citizens, the things society seems to care for most. As a nation, and as individuals, what are we coming to?"

The atmosphere in the hall had become somewhat tense as a result of this dialog. Every one of the teachers was looking inward and feeling some degree of guilt. Apparently emboldened by the riveted attention she was receiving from her colleagues, the speaker continued, "Now that we have matured enough in age to realize our essential worth—or worthlessness—we must recognize that something very important has been missing from our lives."

"What could that be?" inquired Henry, probably rhetorically.

"Why, the spirituality that Master Lam has revealed to us," retorted Christiane. Turning to face Master Lam with an expression illustrating great concern, she said, "We are so thankful for your commentary, Master, but what do we do about it? What do we do now?"

Several nodded. A few turned to others and agreed vocally. All then turned expectantly to Master Lam.

Master Lam had listened to these comments with great interest. He had come to realize that most charlatans in the martial arts—and probably elsewhere—use the arts and conduct their lives on strictly materialistic principles. Looking at the things and people around them, they ask themselves, "Of what immediate use and benefit to myself can I make of these things and people?" In this attitude Master Lam recognized one of the basic differences between the East and the West. Whereas in the East one tends philosophically to turn inward, in the West the direction is outward.

The Master responded to Christiane's question. "I think that at some point in our lives each of us may require a different vision of the world. It is clear to me that you are recognizing that need in yourselves. Mr. Henry has articulated that very clearly. You recognize that it is dishonorable and false for the martial arts teacher to practice so as to attain fame and riches and glory, but you remain puzzled as to what is honorable? You are not at all clear as to *why* you are doing what-you-are-doing as teachers, not clear at all as to what you should be doing, and it is highly probable that spiritually you have been sleep-walking." Master Lam paused. "Am I correct?"

There was silence, but the teachers looked at each other and again nodded.

"Then let me propose this," said the Master. "The basic objective in our advanced training is not technical contrivance. No, not that stuff any more. The basic objective is *to be*. Whereas *to do* means only to perform activities on the superficial layers of our being, *to be* means to delve into the innermost core. We must have a clear understanding of the difference between the two before moving into the last part of our training, the inner transmutation."

Larry spoke up again, "Master, it seems to me that just about everybody in this group feels the same way: What we have been doing is running on the periphery, hiding under the wing of some organization in order to use the organization to justify whatever we do, whether or not our actions are right." Nods of agreement from the group. "The organizations to which we belong do have power to protect us, but I am beginning to realize that the protection they offer is only another aspect of economics: Perhaps they protect what we do in their name so that they can continue to collect the money and power that are generated by 'membership.' Materially we are well-off and successful. We appear to be free. But I believe what you have told us; so, inwardly we are paupers, bound like slaves to the organizations. Our freedom is lost. You have taught us that all conflicts are part of a theatrical scene on a stage, and that we are simply actors. The 'producers' always chart the direction." The teachers clapped their hands, applauding these statements.

Master Lam nodded and pushed the teacher's argument farther. "So one must therefore purify one's consciousness and transcend the mind. Then things may appear as they actually are."

Another young teacher, Gary, put his hands over his face, shaking his head. He sighed, looked up, and addressed Master Lam. "If I did not misunderstand, Master, a while ago you said that what we have learned so far is useless and must be abandoned. Will you elaborate on this, please?"

"At a certain level in your training you must drop all," responded the Master. " When I demonstrate, my words and my movements are only to convey an idea, a form. Once you have grasped the idea, assimilate the form and forget it."

"And forget it?" gasped Yvonne.

"And forget it," replied the Master. "You must understand that truth cannot be taught. You probably have heard martial artists talk about truth, but I am afraid few of them have ever realized it. Talking about truth is only a manifestation of the human tendency to talk about profound things. Talking is not synonymous with realizing. We talk, we brag. Are we not all braggarts?

"Why do I say so? Because, to put it as simply as possible, truth cannot be taught, debated, or exhibited. truth can only be experienced. Such experience is beyond reasoning; it is inexpressible, unexplainable, undefinable. And real knowledge, truth, cannot be borrowed from others. It must be self-constructed. One must work alone to realize truth. Self-realization is first needed. Your teachers and Masters cannot give truth to you, for they are helpless in this arena. Think about this for a moment: If truth can be given, it is a commodity. If it is a commodity, it can be sold."

The thirty-year martial arts veteran, Roland, confessed, "Master, I don't understand how I can, as you say, 'drop all,' forget all my techniques, and remain a teacher. I mean, what then remains for me to teach?"

The Master responded, "There are two answers to the question. If, after years of training, you are able to function creatively in martial art—that is, performing out of your unconscious rather than using your intellect to remember and repeat the old, borrowed stuff of others—then you are growing. Then what it is that you have to teach, by example and by anecdote and analogy and other indirection, is that process of growth.

"If, on the other hand, you are bound to the intellect, to 'officially-sanctioned' forms and movements, then your art is not growing, and what you then have to teach is not worth learning. Remember, please, that things in the world are in flux, nothing is permanent. While we speak the world is moving, changing. You must move with it and beyond those ready-made structures in order to keep up with the changing world."

"Oh, my, now I don't understand at all," said young Gary in a small voice.

The Master cocked his head gently and smiled, then shook his head. "I don't mean that all the techniques you have learned are of no avail. They are still with you, are they not? You don't lose them any more than you lose the sense of riding the bicycle or walking in the woods or lifting cup to lip. You don't lose them, but you must be unburdened of the recollection of them. Only then can you grow. Then you are moving *toward the unknown*, toward the gate of the Divine where genuine creativity waits for you.

"One more consideration. If you refer to yourself as 'creative,' and believe you have created something new and you believe in that creation, then I regret to say that you have invested your belief in something false. For in conceiving and intellectualizing and categorizing, and then of course bragging to yourself about your creativity"—and here the Master smiled and looked about the room for, and received, confirmation of the feeling,— "in so intellectualizing you abolish creativity. Let me explain. Genuine creativity does not come from the intellect, from the conscious mind, but from emptiness, from nowhere—and everywhere. Have you heard me say this before?"

Several of the students nodded.

"My master, Tai-Anh, used to explain that the products of the mind and the products of emptiness are not the same. They are diametrically opposed. One of them deals with observable effects; the other, with one's inner being. If your work has sprung from your mind, that work is but a modification of something you have known with the mind. You partially alter your fantasy in each known form; you change a little bit here and a little bit there from the old routines and you are pleased with that change. But that is a man-made change." The Master paused, smiled, and looked significantly at several teachers. "Or a woman-made change. In either event, it is not natural. A natural change has no bias toward any category of reality, objective or subjective, right or wrong, monistic or dualistic, but is compatible with it. Nature is reality. There is no fixed pattern there. If you see a fixed pattern, creativity must be absent, for genuine creativity abides with no fixed patterns, forms, names. It proceeds out of nowhere, reverts to nowhere."

Gordon spoke, "Master, then we cannot expect when we might reach that creative state, can we?"

"That is true! No such expectation is possible. As I said earlier, we do not really know when and where that quality will be manifested, but we do know that it appears only when one's mind is cleansed of destructive thoughts, of impure materiality, of the illusions in ordinary life. A pure and unstained mind and heart are needed to pursue genuine creativity.

"And be advised: When one has reached the pinnacle of purity and readiness for creativity, one's identity will be lost. One is no longer 'he' or 'she,' but becomes memory-less, a person of no-mind. That loss immediately produces the source of creativity. I ask you to avoid thinking about questions of why, what, where, and how because those questions come from the head-oriented person who calculates with the intellect. The heart-oriented person, on the other hand, works without even knowing those adverbs. Nature endows the heart-oriented person with extraordinary works.

"Creative work, my friends, requires the empty mind. If someone tries to show you his experience in truth, understand that it is a person who has not found it. For if he has indeed found it, he does not try to show it." The Master chuckled. "Is it not true that people have a tendency to show and brag about things they don't really have? When you encounter such a person, consider that ulterior motives may be working.

"Now, I have shown you this much because you have asked me to. What I have shown you is not necessarily the truth, will not be truth until you have internalized it, and perhaps not then. But I saw when I came to this land that martial arts teachers here are very much interested in the superficial: fancy movements, physical tricks, awards, rank, money, the power and influence that comes from organizations that are essentially political. I wish to provide you with a torch of sorts and guide you into the darkness to find your own ways.

"And I do not mean to say that only in this land are martial arts teachers seduced by the superficial. I see this as a world-wide phenomenon."

"So, don't hold or cherish techniques that come from me or others. Don't satiate yourself with words, mine or anyone else's. Better not to embrace a single thing. Learn to let your mind become empty, because in that emptiness beautiful things can come to fill it full.

"Nowadays the temptation is strong to show our students what we know, even though we know nothing. We show new techniques, more techniques, more techniques. Now, what do the students expect of us? Promotion? A certificate? Is this all not a game of ego gratification on the part of both leaders and followers?

Take, for example, the certificate. Does the certificate, nicely signed, with a red chop-mark and perhaps a gold seal and the individual's name in heavy black ink, does this certificate move one toward the *beyond?* I say no. I say that it actually hinders progress, for one never is able to *perform* genuine creativity whatever the certificate may say. Does the certificate ensure security? Definitely not. Then, certificate or no certificate, one remains where one is now. The certificate awarded without the recipient's expecting anything at all is the only true certification. No certificate at all is undoubtedly better!"

The teachers stirred uncomfortably. They had been reared in a society in which, for a very great many of the inhabitants, ethical and moral obligations are confused or absent, and spirituality has become for many either a dualistic blinder or an object of ridicule. Sensuality and worldliness have gained ascendance and have pushed the great majority into feeling great comfort with illusions.

Henry, who had sat silent for a long time now spoke up. "After all of this, shall we blame our Western teachers or our Asian teachers? I suspect that because the martial arts originated in the Orient, that we shall blame our Asian teachers first, for they were the pioneers."

"I believe it is useless, and probably destructive, to blame anyone but ourselves," replied Master Lam. "We have not had the sight, the foresight, or the insight to see things. However, your organization leaders do share some reason for concern, for it is evident that they still run flapping on the periphery, round and round with their egos unfurled. In that state they are unable to shed light that might enter your being. If they have not helped you in the spiritual pursuit of your training, then you are in darkness and, unless you can find the way out, you will remain perpetually in darkness."

Henry spoke for the group. "You have helped us today, Master, but I think it's the feeling of all of us that we want to meet with you again. Right?" He looked about the group and saw affirmation in every face. "Will you honor us again?"

Master Lam bowed. "I am pleased to be here with you, my friends!" he said.

The reception was ended. The participants were quiet, thoughtful. They smiled at Master Lam and spoke quietly among themselves. Master Lam had seen what he believed was a measure of responsiveness in the teachers. Accompanied by Xuan, he returned to the Le residence feeling refreshed.

# 7

# THE DO
# IN MARTIAL ARTS

THE NEXT gathering with Master Lam fell on the day of the twentieth anniversary of Henry's school. Henry was much pleased to have the Master as the honored guest at the event.

The atmosphere of the school was animated. There were more people attending this day, and more new faces appearing on the mat than during the previous gathering. One very noticeable phenomenon was that some of the students and teachers who had left in the middle of Master Lam's lecture last week, now returned with more receptive attitudes. These changes had occurred after only a week of exposure to the "illogical" and "crazy" talk of Master Lam. Strangely such philosophy now begun to make more sense to the hearers.

As is usual with any ceremonial events, Henry began with a short introduction explaining the occasion, welcoming guests, emphasizing the benevolence of the teachers, and pointing to their solidarity in trying to meet some identified needs of the community, as well as the welfare of the students. Henry made a special point of again welcoming his old teacher, Master Lam. On behalf of all the assembled teachers and students, he implored Master Lam to shed more light on some of the problems the Master had identified the week before.

Master Lam took the floor and thanked Henry and the group for inviting him. He began his lecture by giving a brief overview with examples of the universal principles that bond all martial artists, no matter what system of combat to which one subscribes. At the beginning of the Master's demonstrations many members of the audience were still skeptical, but as the Master presented example after example, everyone in the hall acknowledged the Master's theory. All were deeply inspired by his demonstrations.

As the introductory remarks and demonstrations ended and teachers prepared for the workout, the door to the hall burst open and a man staggered in, falling on his knees to the floor, head down, glancing up at Master Lam once or twice through the tangled hair that covered his eyes. Haggard and disheveled, he muttered and appeared intoxicated. The teachers were embarrassed beyond measure, because many recognized the newcomer, but no one moved except Henry who began to approach the intruder.

Master Lam immediately recognized the visitor and

at once advanced toward him across the room. It was The Vanquished, and from his appearance and behavior no one could be sure he had not come to cause mischief. As Master Lam approached him, The Vanquished lowered his head and groaned in a low voice. Master Lam lightly struck a few vital points on the body of The Vanquished, whereupon the miserable intruder collapsed into apparent sleep and was carried off into a side-room to recover his senses. All who saw marveled.

The workout was continued without further interruption, and activity on the mat again became effervescent. Although practitioners of different disciplines were gathered there, they all practiced with eager interest and enthusiasm. They found that the Master's dexterous techniques enlightened them in their own systems. Thus the crux of the workout—the Master's message— was communicated with sophisticated success.

After almost two hours of strenuous exercise, Master Lam asked the participants to rest, and after all had settled down comfortably, the Master said he was ready to answer any questions regarding the training or the art.

Immediately, the confused and curious Casey raised a question that evidently many others had on their minds, for there was much affirmative nodding when the question was asked: "Master, there are so many *do*'s in martial arts: judo, kendo, kyudo, aikido, karatedo, tang soo do, taekwondo, hapkido, jeet kune do, and still others. What do these *do* have in common, if anything? What, if anything, differentiates one from another?"

"I am glad that you asked that question," exclaimed the Master. "I have been thinking about the meanings of *do*, and I'll be happy to elaborate." He smiled. "If you'll be happy to listen carefully, for the answer is not easy to hear! Will you be able to listen carefully?" There was again much affirmative nodding.

The Master closed his eyes and plunged for a moment into deep thought, then began his explanation. "*Do* is a Japanese term." The Master traced the character with his finger. "The character refers to the way or the path. Initially this can be described as the way or the path of how-to, or the path of know-how; that is, how to perform the techniques, how to know the requirements of a particular discipline.

"But the *do* of each discipline includes its own connotation that implies a stringent commitment to mental and/or spiritual pursuit. For you see, each discipline has its own line of direction on which to formulate its *do*. Some disciplines enrich their *do* with dazzling characteristics and a special philosophical "way of life." Others may tint their aims or beliefs with religious concepts. Still others adorn their *do* with extraordinarily flowery rhetoric, jumbling together various ideas from here and there, with the end result that their *do* become unclear, inconsistent, confusing."

The Master looked about the room and saw that while many were paying attention, others were drifting off, unable or unwilling to concentrate on the Master's explanation. "You know," he said pleasantly, looking with a special focus at one young person who had apparently dozed off, "we frequently remind ourselves to eschew thought while we practice our art, to perform out of the unconscious unity of mind and body. However, there are times, in order to help ourselves more easily approach a difficult subject, when it is perfectly all right to use our minds—and stay awake." He shook his head and smiled broadly, still looking at the sleeping student. The participants chuckled, and one nudged the sleeper who awakened, turned bright red, and sat up straight, adjusting his *gi* and looking quite seriously alert.

"Now, as for *do*. Although the *do* of the various martial arts differ from one another in certain respects, generally they represent a basic similarity in their objectives, which are how to improve mind and body, and how to live a human life harmoniously and constructively. This basic communality in which martial artists all share may be described as the Tao of human affairs."

After a short pause, the Master continued, "Anthropologists will tell you that most Asian cultures and value systems have been strongly influenced by Chinese culture mainly through Confucianism, Taoism, and Buddhism; and also by Indian culture. The very character for *do* that Japanese people use nowadays was borrowed into existence from the Taoism of Lao-tsu.

"Lao-tsu's Tao *(do)* has as its original meaning 'that which rises above the common things in the world.' Tao is said to have existed before heaven and earth came into being. It has no like or equal. It is without beginning, without end. In other words, nothing can be compared to it. It is cosmic order, nature, God, The One."

Yvonne raised her hand and asked, "Is the Lao-tsu you're talking about the same one, that legendary figure who is said to have written the *Book of Changes*, the *Tao Te Ching?*"

"Yes, it is he, the most eminent of Chinese sages who lived about 570 B.C., a couple of decades before Confucius, and in the same epoch as that of the Greeks Heraclitus and Pythagoras. Probably Lao-tsu is the first Chinese philosopher who used the word Tao in its specific, constraining designation of the Absolute, Unique Principle of the Universe."

"Master, you used the word 'constraining'?"

"Yes, constraining. Lao-tsu tells us that no other word can possibly communicate this eternal law of nature. Lao-tsu forces himself to term it Tao and then goes on to observe that 'the Tao that can be described is not the eternal Tao; the name that can be named is not the eternal name'." The Master raised his eyebrows. His eyes searched the gathering.

Some of the students appeared lost in these words as the Master, aware of the difficulty for some to comprehend, continued. "Let me try to clarify: In *Tao Te Ching*, Lao-tsu writes that whenever we designate something by means of a name or term, the real entity of that something is at once delimited by that designation. To give a name or a term to something is simply to imply a fragmentary part of Tao. But of course Tao is absolute, unique, an indivisible principle.

"Therefore, in Tao there is neither this nor that, but all, and to provide a name or term to designate a thing is to detract from its entity, its authentic nature. Is that clear?"

There was general nodding of heads about the room.

"Something else very important to consider is this," said the Master. "Whenever Tao is artificially split into qualities such as good and evil or like and dislike, a duality is created, and the spiritual life of the person who is doing the splitting is diminished. The truth of a person is beyond the concept of duality."

"Master," cried one student who had been able to follow this argument, "How can one do away with the concepts of good and evil, like and dislike, when they are so, so, so . . . useful?"

"Ah, thank you! One is not able to 'do away' with such perceptions except by transcending them. First, one must be aware in order to be able to comprehend that any 'this' or 'that' are really parts of the same phenomenon. And then, one must learn to accept and transcend.

"You said the terms 'good' and 'evil' are useful?" The Master looked at the student in a kindly way and said gently, "But I must respond that such 'usefulness' actually constitutes error, and that as one accepts such separation and division, one departs from spirituality, and the divine oneness is lost, truth is lost."

"We must accept evil?"

"If you are to become at one with the Tao, you must learn to accept and transcend such labels," said the Master. "To become at one with the Tao, you must understand that all behavior is 'natural' and part of The One. This does not mean, in practical terms, that you must accept behavior in others that is harmful to you. Only keep in mind that whenever you dwell in the present moment, as long as you think in terms of duality, such as good and evil, like and dislike, comfort and discomfort, you remove yourself from truth.

"And will you continue to wish fervently to live forever, desire wealth, prefer the sunny to the rainy season? Well, as you continue to wish for these things, your expectations will mount, and their failure will become your frustration."

"Ah, Master," said Roland, a competent and sincere teacher, "it seems that everything we are comfortable with in this world becomes a source of frustration for us eventually."

"So true! So true!" said the Master, approvingly. "It is partly a problem of language, you know. The very instant you speak up in order to give something a meaning, a definition, you limit it, you restrict it. In doing so, you pull it away from wholeness. And you pull yourself away from being able to understand its wholeness. Ah, the Tao is so elusive. Remember, Tao holds both opposites. Thus, with words as one mentions right, the very mention adheres error within itself. How then are we to arrive at being able to identify absolute wrong or absolute right?"

"How, Master?" asked several at once. The young Burt said, "Oh, my! I don't understand this at all."

The Master smiled and sighed. "Remember this: words are limited, fixed, stationary; that is, dead. The Tao is always alive and changes incessantly. Incessantly: 'without cessation.' For this reason, the Tao cannot be explained in words, and therefore words cannot be used to identify that which can not be defined by words. Are you with me?"

The student who was so frustrated said, "Ah!" Then, "But, Master, people keep on talking about Tao and explaining it. I mean, we're talking about it here and now. Isn't that strange?"

"Well," responded the Master, "useless, perhaps, but not strange, for human beings like to use what they have. And often the most satisfying way to use what one has is to, how does one say it? to 'show off'.

"Now, that showing off may not be a particularly worthy thing, but human beings do it. And when martial arts teachers do it, alas, it seems it is only a bait to bring something into the teaching that might engage the interest of the students. Isn't that what is called nowadays, 'motivating the student'?" The Master smiled a very small smile.

"I must confess to you that I do see some of you in that light, my young friends."

"How, Master? How do you see us?" clamored several of the teachers, delighted that Master Lam had been "thinking about" them, but also worried about the direction the Master's lesson seemed to be taking.

"You want to hear about it, to see it in action, to learn it, to grasp it," replied Master Lam. "However, it takes courage to leave all that aside and simply be it. I ask myself, 'Do they yet have the courage to be it? Do they yet have the audacity to go inward, into their inner being?'"

There was a lengthy silence. Several in the audience looked at each other. Several looked at the mat. Some closed their eyes. Others looked in puzzlement at the Master. No one said a word until finally one student broke the spell, "How may one be it, Master?"

"First, in your daily living be receptive. Do not distinguish between like and dislike, happy and unhappy, lucky and unlucky. Simply be receptive: accept what is in total calmness. Let your senses melt in your heart in this acceptance-without-discrimination and you will have become it. Then you are it. You are with the Tao, for you then have gone beyond the boundaries of opposites—without thinking about having done it!

"You have then known something. However, that kind of knowing of that something is so subtle, so delicate that it is ineffable, and trying to put it into words—even the words that would enable you to talk to yourself about your experience—trying to put it into words will cause your knowing to disappear!"

The Master looked down at his folded hands, opened them, looked at them open, and raised his eyes to the students. "How foolish of me," he said in a very quiet voice. "How foolish of me to try to explain Tao. How dare I!"

Of course, as he himself recognized, Master Lam erred in trying to use words to explain Tao. But he also illustrated the near universality of the temptation to try, for even those who know better will occasionally succumb to that temptation, thinking that perhaps they are able to effect the short-cut to something that can be conceived by short-cut only via the intuition.

Even as he erred and recognized his error, the Master began reciting the words of Chuang-tsu:

"'Tao cannot be heard, and being heard is no longer Tao; Tao cannot be told, and being told is no longer Tao.'"

Looking at his students, the Master continued, "You should understand that the one who asks about Tao, as well as the one who answers the question, both must be ignorant of Tao. Nevertheless, if the *do* in martial arts really concerns you—and I think it does—then the following is what I think.

"In the field of martial arts the *do* that you are eager to know appears to have recently superseded the term *jutsu*, which means technique. *Jutsu* as a guiding principle had been found no longer appropriate to the dignity and true meaning of martial arts. Practiced in a turbulent society, a society full of deceit, unfairness, aggression, and the like, *jutsu*, instead of providing stability, had contributed to the overthrow of long-accepted ethical and moral values, and had led people to live hectic and confused lives."

"So we don't use *jutsu* any more, Master?" concluded Casey, the confused teacher.

"The term *jutsu* no longer has a connection with Tao. Clear-sighted masters came to realize that merely focusing on technical ability in martial arts was not only not conducive to good morale and the general well-being of students, such a focus actually contributed to bad morale and ill-health.

"Unfortunately, most practitioners seem indifferent to the distinction and unconcerned about it. It is as if the distinction had never been made. Many practitioners seem addicted to the pursuit of *jutsu*. And I see this as regression." The Master shook his head sadly. "Regrettable, regrettable. No matter what your martial arts discipline, emphasize the *do*, for *jutsu* is simply a means, not an end. Remember, my friends, the Path is not something you do; it is something that you become."

The Master looked up and a broad smile creased his face as he formulated some visual examples for the group. He raised his arms and illustrated his talk with gestures. "Consider *jutsu* to be the boat you have borrowed to reach the other shore of the lake. When you arrive on that shore, leave the boat there and continue on your journey. The boat is simply a means. Means are many; the end is one.

"Serious travelers toward The One are few because most of the travelers are dilettantes. Dilettantes are extroverts who participate in the art for amusement, as a pastime rather than as contemplation. Dilettantes look outward; they avoid seeking the inward. They seek technical tricks, decorations, and awards that help satisfy their egos—and perhaps their ulterior motives.

"The sincere practitioner is quite different. The sincere practitioner is not an exhibitionist, does not practice as entertainment. The sincere practitioner—perhaps we could more accurately use the phrase 'authentic practitioner'—the authentic practitioner works toward deepening thought, feeling, spirit."

The Master was silent. He looked at the group, from one to another, a patient, questioning expression on his face, as much as to say, "Are you comprehending?"

And a good many of the students responded to his questioning looks with nods and smiles. The Master had apparently succeeded in communicating the idea that while the objective aspect of training in martial arts—technique—has become the more attractive, the subjective aspect—the spiritual—must be present as well. For one without the other is like the image impressed into only one side of the coin: A one-sided coin may as well exist only as novelty.

The Master pursued the point. "Understanding the *do*, or talking about the *do*, is quite different from following the *do*. For to follow the *do*, one must live with it in order to experience it. And to experience it requires long and hard work, requires the enduring of the vicissitudes of the training. Only with great diligence and after long, painstaking periods of time is one able to achieve something worthwhile.

"There is no shortcut. If the modern mind can be described as having one most acute disease, it may well be that people prefer the easy way. That one disease might be termed 'the shortcut.' One cannot experience the *do* via the shortcut."

In reviewing the lesson the Master reminded the

group that *jutsu* and *do*—the objective and subjective—are not separable from each other; they are but two aspects of the same phenomenon. That which is hidden, the *do*, the subjective, has to do with the inner training in which the spirit is cultivated and nurtured from the very beginning of the training. This spirituality is the very cornerstone of Asian martial arts.

The Western world, the Master observed, is immersed in a powerful urge to look for its greatness in the objective, in externals, the world of phenomena. Perhaps it is this materialistic emphasis that in the Western world—and in those elements of the Eastern world that now have been so profoundly influenced by the West—eats away at the emotional and spiritual aspects of human life. Perhaps, observed the Master, one should ponder this problem with an eye to making some inner changes.

"In short," said Master Lam, sitting up straight and raising his voice from the low-pitched contemplative tone he had been using, "in short, we can say that the *do* in martial arts has to do with how ethics and morality enhance spirit. As martial artists, we cannot tramp about on the periphery of the spiritual, pleasing ourselves with appearance. For unless we leave surface things behind, we are never able to gain the center, the root of our being and the source of our art."

Roland asked once again, "Master, I have been pursuing martial arts studies for decades now and have sat with any number of teachers and masters, but none until today ever brought to my attention the crucial point you just raised. Have I not been listening? Have all these other teachers a different way of looking at martial art? Is their teaching of such a radically different style?"

"Ah," said the Master, "perhaps you had not met the right teacher. Or perhaps you had not asked the questions that stimulated the responses you have heard today. Or perhaps their own training was limited to *jutsu* with never a mention of *do*. It is easy to blame your teachers, but of course it is useless and self-deceptive. Examine your own behavior and expectations. Have you not been dazzled by appearance and have you not sought flashy technique and enjoyed spectacle?

"Further, think on this: I have here two small wooden boxes of the same size." Master Lam mimed having boxes before him. He held first one up, then the other, examining them. "Listen. When I knock on this one, a loud sound resounds throughout the room. When I knock on this other, there is hardly any sound at all.

"From our experience with such things, do we already know something about the loud-sounding box? Yes, of course, that it is empty. And of the quiet box? That it is absolutely full of something. Consider further: With human enterprises, do we use the lesson we have learned about the sound of the boxes?"

The young Burt laughed aloud. "We surely do not, Master. We look at he who makes the biggest noise, and we pay not the slightest attention to the quiet one!"

And Gary said, "Ah, I understand. I understand the point the Master is trying to make!"

Yet Gordon spoke up. "But isn't it also true, Master,

that in a democratic society, the majority rules, and what the majority believes is desirable is promoted, and expands, and becomes ever more influential with the masses?"

"Yes, yes," responded Master Lam. "But keep in mind that the value of an idea, of a belief, of a way is not determined by *how many* people believe it and follow it. The majority may believe that the world is flat. Indeed, just look about and you will have the proof of that proposition before your eyes. But for all of that supposed proof, the world is not flat; and no matter how many of our contemporaries celebrate its flatness, the world will not conform with that belief."

There was silence again in the *dojo* as the students pondered the Master's words. "You may be sincerely, earnestly with the majority," he continued, "and of course even the minority is bound to the majority and for practical reasons usually must follow it, for the majority rules. And that majority can be absolutely wrong, corrupt, despicable, and yet rule in the approval of all. Read your history books.

"But there is a law that is separate from both the idea of majority or minority. It is an internal law, a voice that speaks within each of us who has cultivated it. It is conscience, an ethical and moral virtue that impels every one of us toward right thought and right action."

The Master's lips curved in a wry smile. "Let me tell you a story about majority rule, unexamined majority rule, *consensus gentium*, 'the opinion of the people.' I believe the story will stimulate some insight.

"There was once a festival in a small community. A restaurateur was hired to prepare food and drink for about fifty persons, all the town's upper-crust. On the eve of the festival, the restaurateur had a dream in which he was warned that the water supply of the restaurant was poisoned. He awoke in a sweat and convinced his brother to go to the neighboring community and bring back a supply of pure water.

"On the day of the festival, the restaurateur opened the doors of the restaurant even though the brother still had not yet returned with the pure water supply. The nobility ate breakfast at the restaurant, drank the contaminated water, and became deranged—wailing, screaming, falling down, beating their heads on the table, and throwing bowls at one another.

"The owner, having of course been forewarned by the dream, did not drink the water and so remained calm, sober, sedate, watching the madness that began in his restaurant and then spread to the streets outside as the nobility left the restaurant.

"The deranged nobility saw the calm and collected owner and pointed at him: 'Madman! Madman!' they shouted and bound him and were determined to throw him in the town jail.

"Now quite as might be expected, the restaurateur detested the idea of being thrown thus into jail. At first he was perplexed as to what to do. But then he looked at the anxiety and pain and confusion in the eyes of his wife and children, all of whom had consumed the bad water. He made his decision, and at once consumed a cup of the contaminated water. Quickly he began to foam at the mouth and rave and sing.

"'Ah,' said the nobility of the town, 'Our host is better. In fact, now he is perfectly all right. No need to take him into custody after all.' And the nobility pardoned the restaurateur for his sin then and there. He was no longer mad, for he was now on the side of the raving nobility. He was with the majority. He was safe in the mad world."

Master Lam laughed. The students did not, though some smiled pensively, waiting for the Master's further comment. The Master's face became serious again. "You see," he said, "One must decide whether being with the majority is worth the price you must pay when you know the majority is wrong. One must decide if it's worth the price you must pay when you see corruption and dishonesty and yet hold your peace.

"And what is that price? Of course the price you pay for being with an erroneous majority is your loss of authenticity, honor, integrity, by which I mean your ethical wholeness."

The Master then said, "Now, what of the brother who was sent for wholesome water, he who failed to appear in time? Let us speculate that he did finally reappear and saw the madness all around him, the madness that now included the restaurateur. And let us further speculate that the brother refused to drink the polluted water, in spite of threats to his person and even though pressed to do so by everyone, including the owner.

"Now such resolve, such following of one's conscience is virtuous, beautiful, right! It is the action of an authentic human being. The brother acted according to the direction of his heart, and so he was at ease despite the threats of the majority.

"But we may speculate also on the price the brother had to pay for his exercise of conscience. How pitiable and unfortunate is often the fate of the minority! Their conscience-driven deeds may be considered stupid or wrong-headed by the majority. Their benevolence, their honesty, may be seen by the majority as provocative, insulting, anti-social.

"But consider both the majority and the virtuous minority: Which are more likely to be at one with Tao?"

Although their physical exercise had been vigorous this day, and the seated discussion had proceeded for some time now, the students gave no sign of fatigue or that they were otherwise eager to leave the *dojo*.

But the Master said, "Perhaps we should remove ourselves for the day and return later, early this afternoon for another workout," said the Master. "Shall we do that, or would you like to pursue our discussion a bit longer?"

"By all means," said the group, "let us stay a bit. I for one am eager to hear more." Others agreed, and the Master re-settled himself.

"Very well," said Master Lam. "A few minutes more. So, consider this: A man deludes another, collecting money and delivering shoddy goods to the purchaser.

The seller is confronted and accused of cheating. He replies, 'Hah! So what! It's not illegal!' And he is correct. His false claims were merely exaggerations and, anyway, could not be proved in a court of law.

"Cheating, duping, deluding others for profit are acts of bad faith. They are no less evil if such acts are within the law. The fact that the man apparently recognized that he was cheating (for he did say 'So what! It's not illegal!), that fact tells us that the cheater had no conscience. So what does such a story tell us?" asked Master Lam.

There was a long silence. Finally, Christiane responded, "Master, I think it means that when deciding right from wrong, a person who is morally mature relies on her ability to deliberate and examine her conscience, and then makes the decision regardless of whether it will be approved or disapproved by others." She looked at Master Lam questioningly, her eyebrows raised.

"Are you seeking my approval of your answer?" the Master asked, his eyes twinkling. All laughed, and Christiane blushed and nodded her head. "Let the world go to the utmost in madness, it will eventually return to sanity. One must know how to yield during the madness, how to yield and how to wait-and-see.

"Consider this saying of Lao-tsu: 'Under the Heaven all can see beauty as beauty only because of the existence of ugliness. All can know good only because of the existence of evil.'

"We constantly encounter such contrasts, do we not?

These contrasts are the root cause of disorder in the world. That is why Lao-tsu suggests that in such circumstances we must 'do nothing.'"

The students looked at each other in puzzlement, some shaking their heads discreetly. Yvonne spoke up, "Master, several times we have heard you speak of 'doing nothing.' Is not 'doing nothing' in the face of evil a profoundly pessimistic act, an anti-human attitude, not to speak of being cowardly? I am confused, confused, Master!"

The Master sighed. "We are speaking of Tao, and as we know, in speaking of Tao we lose it. We are attempting to define in words the ineffable. But, foolishly, we shall try. Let us take up this question this afternoon, for I see that you need time to accept, to yield, to enjoy your confusion!" The Master closed the morning session, smiling to himself.

# 8

# SELF-IMPROVEMENT AND CONVERSION

DURING BREAK-TIME, Master Lam entered the room where The Vanquished remained in deep sleep. The Master released the vital points he had fixed in the body of The Vanquished two hours earlier.

It was apparent to the Master that The Vanquished had come to Henry's school to seek him, probably hoping for a reconciliation, forgiveness, a return to honor. The prospect of facing the Master was daunting and the need for the courage offered by alcohol was the stupid route The Vanquished had chosen. However stupidly the route was chosen, The Vanquished had at least begun that difficult journey away from error.

Now, as he was awakened from his sleep, The Vanquished felt calm, placid. "Strange," he thought, "My head does not throb. My body feels wonderful for the first time in years." At once he knelt submissively before the Master, head lowered, smitten with remorse.

He hesitated for a moment, then said, "Master, I feel deep shame. I regret not keeping my vow to return to your service as I promised. My disrespect, my rudeness, and my arrogance have caused me much pain and trouble over the years. I don't know what to do. I don't know how to make amends to you for my wrongdoing. Forgive me, Master. Teach me, please. I want to be changed. I want to be transformed. Is it too late, Master?"

Master Lam regarded The Vanquished sternly, but he had now heard self-reproach and a confession from this man. Maintaining the stern expression, Master Lam spoke, "Your having abandoned the solemn vow you made is one of the most dishonorable of acts in the field of martial arts. You must know that." The Vanquished shuddered, nodded, his head down.

"However," continued the Master, "you have recognized your errors and you now appear contrite. I believe you are sincere. But of course repentance such as yours amounts only to words."

The Vanquished looked up, pain in his eyes. He began to speak but the Master raised his hand for silence.

"Your promise, the vow you took, was also only words. Shall I trust your words again?" The Master looked away, apparently thinking. The Vanquished watched, now tense. The Master turned again toward the kneeling figure. "If you really want to convince me of your complete repentance, then you must put that repentance into practice. Actions count here, not words. Words you can change any time. At any moment you may use words to make a superficial change, but deep down inside you may remain unchanged.

"Your essential action must be to change your being. Then the peripheral things will follow." The brows of The Vanquished knitted; he was not comprehending. The Master pursued the point. "I might array myself in a fine, impressive garment, but that does not necessarily mean that I have suddenly become 'somebody.' I might affect and announce a great and important title, but that does not mean that I am 'somebody.' Apparel and titles are superficialities, understand? The assumption of authority does not validate authority. Even as I put on fine apparel and sport a great title and assume authority, I run the grave risk of believing my self-created illusion, of becoming authoritarian, not authoritative. I risk becoming not only wrong-headed, but arrogant as well. When in such a condition I get others to follow me, I then become a leader of the sightless and the thoughtless. And does that make me 'somebody'?" The Master drew close to The Vanquished and looked deep into his eyes. "What is true for me is true also for everybody else," The Master said. "It is true for you."

A long silence ensued, neither the Master nor The Vanquished moving. Finally The Vanquished looked up. "Master," he said, "please tell me what to do to get back in your good graces." He said other things, too, all of them beseeching the Master to "fix" him, make him "better."

The beseeching appeared to Master Lam to be sincere, honest, and he decided to try the classic approach with those who have strayed from the honorable path. "Well, all right, we'll see."

The Vanquished sat up straight, evidently much relieved. "Now, what do I say?" he asked the Master.

Master Lam shook his head slightly before answering. "It's not what one says, but what one does that has value. You have been making grand, bold statements all your life, and to what end have you come? No, if you want to become a martial arts teacher . . ."

"But, Master, I am already a martial arts teacher?"

"Ah, as evidenced by your behavior, you are merely a fairly competent technician. In order to become a teacher you must begin cultivating, demonstrating honesty, sincerity, uprightness. Demonstrating, not merely proclaiming.

"From all accounts your behavior has been clearly selfish. It has been greedy. It has been arrogant and boorish. Such behavior is a barrier to any advancement in one's martial arts status. You do not deserve to be recognized as a teacher."

This was all news to The Vanquished who, while having harbored a few private reservations about his own prowess, nevertheless had usually envisioned himself overall as a splendid fellow.

As if he had been reading the thoughts of The Vanquished, Master Lam announced, "To deserve to be recognized as a teacher of martial arts, you must improve your personality." The face of The Vanquished darkened, fell. The Master continued, "It is never too late to do this."

The face of The Vanquished was now slack-jawed. He hung his head, looking at the mat.

"Do you know what 'personality' means?" inquired the Master. There was no answer, only a puzzled expression. "It means the quality of being a person, a human being different from other species. It is expressed in the way you walk, talk, act, express yourself, feel—and teach." Master Lam paused and looked with narrowed eyes at The Vanquished. "Are you ready to take these things into consideration and put them into an improved practice?"

The Vanquished did not reply at once. He closed his eyes, as if considering deeply. Good, thought the Master, this may be the first step.

Then The Vanquished raised his head and spoke. "Master," he said, "as I have traveled about the world I have acquired a lot of 'baggage.' I now have a wild mode of living. I have lots of bad habits, really bad habits, I think. I guess." He paused, struck his fist into his palm. "I mean, I know I have. When I think about it I realize that I have created all kinds of troubles for my family and for the people around me. When I think about it more, I realize that in my teaching I have probably created problems for my students, also for society." His head drooped once again, and his posture slumped. "I doubt that it is possible for me to improve in all the qualities you just named. I don't know. I don't know." He shook his head.

"You are the only one who does know," countered Master Lam. "But I believe that, although you will not be able to slough off your bad habits overnight, nevertheless with self-discipline and will-power and attentiveness, you can at least begin quickly to show improvement in those qualities. Following the precepts I have identified, you will then pave the way for your own improvement. As is always true in martial arts, everything depends on you."

The posture of The Vanquished once again improved, and he looked hopefully, questioningly, at Master Lam.

"At the same time you are working on your specific self-improvement," continued the Master, "it is important for you to maintain good relationships with teachers who are decent persons, who are outstanding teachers, authentic teachers."

"But how do I recognize these teachers? Who are these authentic teachers, Master?"

"Henry, the head of this school, is the best I have known in this land," responded Master Lam. "The first, best test of your ability to change might be your willingness to subordinate yourself to his influence."

The Vanquished thought a moment. "I believe I can do that."

"It may be more difficult than you think for, as you have said, you have a history of bad habits. You must break those habits."

"Yes, I understand," said The Vanquished.

"All right," said the Master. "Here is some advice to take to heart, if you will persist in teaching:

• Try always to be humble

- Speak little, let your words be expressed in action
- Do not try to 'control' people, relate with them on the basis of equality
- Do not hold *others* to rules and regulations; attend to your own acts
- Try to be a virtuous example for others
- Constantly examine your own behavior
- When you catch yourself in a selfish act, reverse yourself
- When you catch yourself being proud and arrogant, step back, reconsider, regain silence
- Cultivate a benign facial expression, for by that means you may help your conscious behavior to follow."

Master Lam paused a minute or so then slowly continued, "The martial arts are in a state of moral decline, and today you have agreed to bear a share of responsibility to restore their tone. One final important thing. You practiced your art in Asia. When you behave shamefully you bring that shame upon your identity as an Asian teacher. You cause others to question the authenticity of the classical martial arts training. Remember well, one who feels no shame at shameful acts does not deserve to be known as human."

Master Lam had hit upon two psychological points that required that The Vanquished feel he was responsible for the decline in martial arts and for the respect worthiness of the Asian teacher. These two points deeply touched the spirit of valor that remained alive deep within The Vanquished, and he thus felt that if he could be responsible, then he must be of some worth, too.

He now looked upon Master Lam as upon one invested with a mysterious power. He prostrated himself repeatedly before the Master, finally bloodying his head and face in the process. Master Lam looked on impassively.

Such impassivity in the Master at this point may seem to the ignorant, to be excessively harsh and unloving and not at all in that spirit of loving kindness about which the Master so often spoke. But it is important to remember that one's choices, as for example this self-prostration of The Vanquished, may be the only way one is able to pave the road to awakening. This transaction between The Vanquished and the Master, with the Master apathetic on the outside and compassionate within, and The Vanquished trying symbolically to demonstrate his ability to beat the shame from himself, is a deeply Asian trait.

The Vanquished is demonstrating submission, the act of a person determined to comply with an order, showing firm intention, all for a change in his self. "History has once again repeated itself," the Master thought. One is reminded of the tale of Shen-kuang.

The monk Shen-kuang came to implore Bodhidharma to teach him Dharma (truth), but Bodhidharma remained silent, facing the stone wall in practice of *pi-kuan* (wall-contemplation). Shen-kuang begged a number of times to be taught but Bodhidharma did not budge. Hours passed and it began to snow. When snow rose to

Shen-kuang's knees, he still stood, waiting, but there was no response from Bodhidharma.

Shen-kuang then cut off his left arm to demonstrate his sincerity and his determination. Bodhidharma began then to speak to him. Later, Shen-kuang achieved enlightenment, received the Buddhist name Hui-ke, and became Second Patriarch of Chinese Ch'an (Zen) Buddhism.

Although the inchoate penitence of The Vanquished cannot begin to compare with the bloody sacrifice of Shen-kuan, it will be recognized that The Vanquished did show some willingness to learn, to change. Were this willingness to persist, the Master knew, then life for The Vanquished would begin to bloom and flower in a new dimension.

Master Lam bade The Vanquished to sit and provided him with a new name, An-nan (The Repentant). He directed An-nan to return to the school in the afternoon, but to take part in the gathering only as an observer.

An-nan returned home that afternoon in an exalted mood. Unexpectedly, he felt extremely frightened, frightened for an unknown reason that tangled his mind. At once, a minute of turbulence hit him and he attacked everything that was before him, throwing to the floor cups, books, a lamp, trophies on the shelves and awards as well as certificates from the walls—things he had yesterday rejoiced in.

An-nan demolished everything in his room. Obviously, the wild temperament had not departed from the poor man, though he had vowed to conduct himself like everyone else.

After that brief madness, An-nan sank into an armchair that remained not-quite-demolished. Sitting there quietly he recalled the words of Master Lam. It was not too late for him to make a change or to improve his personality, but that he must exert a strong will-power to overcome the various obstacles. Nobody could help him but himself, he recalled Master Lam saying. The directives of Master Lam wandered through An-nan's consciousness, mingled with other thoughts, and An-nan began to laugh uncontrollably. He shouted again and again, "It's not too late, it's not too late!"

Gradually the shouting moderated to a mumble, and An-nan fell asleep in his chair. Outside, the sky was dark with low clouds. Rain began to fall as if it partook in An-nan's affliction.

# THAT'S IT: NOTHING!

ALL THE PARTICIPANTS felt that the evening workout was quite exciting. Each one seemed to concentrate on finding different ways of performing techniques with which they had been long familiar. The members rolled and jumped, falling and rising, moving with attractive grace. The scene on the mat appeared lively and lovely indeed.

Although the practitioners employed a great variety of recognizably formal movements—dodging, defending, attacking, and counter-attacking—they began to display a blending and a spontaneous responsiveness that they had previously lacked. They had unconsciously stepped over the threshold of emptiness and moved into a world that inwardly rendered them qualitatively different. Truly they had grown!

In one corner of the mat a kung-fu teacher performed

some kind of *kote gaeshi*. In another corner an *aikidoka* circled her arms around in pulling her opponent, and ended gracefully with a movement similar to *tai otoshi*. The *judoka* across the mat jumped in the air and landed adroitly in a position that looked very much like a kung-fu *the-dragon-lands-on-the-ocean*. Nearby, a *karateka* performed a movement resembling *wave-hands-in-the-cloud*. Others appeared in their movements to include some of the essentials of *peng, lu, chi, an* . . . the ward-off, roll back, press, and pull down of t'ai-chi ch'uan.

As to the style in which they were performing, truly these forms could not be identified with any style. The movements somehow embraced all styles. The forms were formless, nameless. For one who had grasped the essence of the art, the forms varied, transformed, and then lost their exclusivity. One could say only that a particular movement was reminiscent of a particular style, nothing more.

Standing in a corner of the training hall, Master Lam smiled discreetly. To himself he said the words, "That's it." Without seeking, the students had discovered and were participating in the mystery. Master Lam had successfully turned the group from the periphery to the center, then helped them to move from the inside and let it flow to the outside. The transmutation had occurred. "That's it," said the Master.

Untrained people can see the beauty in the forms of martial arts, but how many can see the beauty of the formless? Appreciating the beauty of the form is akin to browsing on the surface; the experience is ephemeral.

Seeing the beauty of the formless is entering into the core, the source; its experience is eternal.

After the evening workout, followed by a light supper, the group gathered around the Master in the garden where the sun had recently disappeared through the pines, leaving the garden in a pale golden glow. The birds that usually sang in the garden were now still. All contemplated the beauty of the place. Yvonne broke the silence and the mood with the comment, "Well, we're doing nothing, Master!" Everyone chuckled.

"You know," said the Master, "most people profoundly misunderstand these words—'doing nothing.' As is typical with words, the phrase doesn't mean quite what it sounds like it means. After all, if Lao-tsu meant that to do nothing equals inactivity, absence of action, he would never have composed the *Tao-te Ching*.

"In that masterpiece Lao-tsu says that he has three treasures. The first is mercy, the second frugality, and third is not to dare to be ahead of others.

"Mercy is a compassionate forbearance one shows toward all without distinguishing the good and the bad. However, people in this world are not merciful in that sense, are they? They insist on repaying an injury with what?"

"An injury!" shouted Burt.

"An injury. And an evil with an evil. This is the vulgar way, the common doing. Mercy, remember, is daring to treat the adversary as a friend, and not acting on an enemy in revenge, not treating an adversary to an evil. Mercy means not igniting the thought of hatred. It means ignoring the very meaning of the word 'hatred.'

"While people in the world typically identify luxury and ostentation as goals representing success in life, Lao-tsu advises not to strive to be ahead of others, but instead be modest. He advises us to be humble and use frugality as our basis for any dealing. So, to Lao-tsu, mercy, frugality, and forbearance are the three treasures of doing nothing.

"In the ordinary course of world affairs, action—that is, *being*—employs power to overcome power. The non-action way—the way of non-*being*—employs gentleness to overcome hardness, feebleness to overcome strength. Using non-action to win is winning without fighting. This is the do-nothing of Lao-tsu.

"People in the world who contend for power and profit do so to inflate their egos. To them, more power and profit are manifested by collecting and accumulating wealth and authority. The more the better. Lao-tsu, on the contrary, advises to live simply, naturally, and to try to avoid avarice. The more one gives to others, Lao-tsu suggests, the more one possesses.

"Furthermore, Lao-tsu advises, do not think of yourself as bright. Do not consider yourself right. Do not claim credit for things accomplished. And when these are not thought, considered, or claimed, then brightness, rightness, and accomplishments remain with you. These are the doing-nothings of Lao-tsu."

The Master's discourse bewildered his common-sense audience. He saw that many appeared distraught. The Master felt then that he must explain further.

"Do nothing does not mean that you fold your arms and wait for the result. Do nothing means that you function without manipulating, without straining, without excessive striving; it means that you conduct your life in a natural, careful, and unselfish manner—and let things take their natural course and accomplish their own ends."

"But Master," said Casey, "this sounds most paradoxical. You said do things in a natural, unselfish, careful manner and let things take their own course. 'Natural' and 'unselfish' seem contradictory. Does 'unselfish' as you use the word mean 'disinterested,' 'altruistic'? What does it mean?

The Master replied, "It means letting the natural disposition of one's being act as it will. The doing must have no ulterior motive. The doing must be like the doing of the sun, radiating its light to the multitude of flowers—without intending or being conscious of the benefits of its radiation. And like the flowers, too, simply do, not thinking about, or even being aware of their dependence on the rays of the sun. They simply bloom.

"In human affairs, the non-doing grantor of favor, like the sun, doesn't consider the power of the granting, doesn't even realize the act itself; and the grantee, the receiver of the favor, does not consider the favor as favor. The virtue of the act of granting of favor, like the virtue of the sunray is the doing-of-nothing. No activity is undertaken, and yet there is nothing left undone!"

The students were still confused and looked at each other with baffled expressions. The Master pursued the point, "Let me try to explain, using these words again!

In the practice of medicine, students used to take an oath in which they pledged to consecrate their lives to the service of humanity. Do you believe such an oath is necessary?" The Master did not wait for the response, but continued. "If the oath is necessary, it is then also meaningless, the words mere noises. Why?

"Well, I shall tell you. If at the outset, the medical students know that their study will lead them in the life-long service of humanity, and that their first consideration for all their existence will be the comfortable birthing, healthful living, and dignified dying of their patients, then the students will pursue the study of medicine wholeheartedly, earnestly, sincerely. They will be authentic students and have no need for promises, no need to swear oaths before audiences and over sacred texts."

"But, Master, we all need to swear our allegiance to government, to our mates, to our employers," said Casey. "I mean, that's what we've always done. It's expected!"

"It may be expected," said the Master. "It may be what you have always done. But swearing oaths is only adhering to custom or meeting social obligation. It is a formality, not a natural act. Remember, I speak of authenticity. When people of virtue see the need for their participation in humanitarian enterprises, they simply do. They allow their consciences to follow the natural path, not aiming to serve, neither swearing oaths nor attempting to prove themselves to others, but only to act without ulterior motive."

"Master," cried Casey again in some alarm, "are you denying the worth of the Hippocratic Oath? If physicians do not take that required oath, they cannot legitimately work in the service of humanity."

"Ah. Well, I pose to you this question," responded the Master. "Does the taking of the oath provide us with physicians who are committed to medical virtue?"

"Yes, of course," said several members, nodding to each other.

"If I hear you correctly, then, the oath-taking weeds out of medicine those practitioners who might otherwise prove to be venal, money-grubbing, cruel, egotistic, head-oriented and not heart-oriented. The taking of the oath certifies only the virtuous, and we therefore suffer no venal or cruel or money-grubbing, head-not-heart-oriented physicians?"

"Oh," said several teachers at once, "Well, there are venal physicians despite the oath. And money-grubbing physicians, too. And perhaps cruel, conscienceless, and egotistic ones, too"

"Ah," said the Master. "Well then, perhaps it is *not* the swearing of an oath that generates virtuous, heart-oriented behavior; that is, behavior that is loving, humane, compassionate?

The group was silent again. In the darkness the fireflies glowed.

Speaking in a soft voice the Master broke the silence. "The mother loves her child. Should the child fall into danger, the mother rushes to rescue. No oath binds a mother to rescue her child who is in danger. The mother simply rushes in without thought to save her child. No one has urged the mother to behave in a 'motherly' way. Nor is she trying to impress anyone with her 'motherliness.' She simply acts.

"But of course this is a non-action, a doing-nothing that emanates from the bottom of the heart. And this is the action of the heart-oriented person I referred to a moment ago. To sum up, doing nothing is returning action to its source. Doing nothing is discarding all complicated things such as the deceptive artifices that conceal the genuine characteristics of the natural human disposition. Lao-tsu said, 'The pursuit of learning is the acquisition of something day by day. The pursuit of Tao is dropping something day by day, dropping and dropping until there is nothing left to drop. When nothing remains to drop, no action remains to be undertaken, nothing is left undone.'"

"Hm," said several teachers to themselves. Others turned to their fellows and nodded their heads. Then Casey, again, said to the Master, "Master, earlier you said something about Tao, about talking about Tao. Could you tell us again?"

The Master smiled. "I said all that can be said about Tao, is that the one who asks about Tao, as well as the one who answers about it, both are ignorant of it. Remember that?"

Everyone nodded, *Yes*.

"Then hear this: Tao cannot be heard. Being heard, it is no longer Tao. I tell you this: Tao cannot be told. Being told, it is no longer Tao. In living a virtuous life, a life emanating from the heart, you shall come as close to Tao as ones who without seeking it can come. Simply live; live simply. Accept. Be loving, humane, compassionate. Our martial arts provide us with a marvelous vehicle for expressing our virtue spiritually and morally as well as physically."

"Master, have you now revealed to us the secret of the relationship of the martial arts and Tao?" said Yvonne eagerly.

The Master sighed, hesitated a moment gazing at the large yellow moon now rising, and answered quietly and with a smile, "Hear this: Tao cannot be heard. Being heard, it is no longer Tao. I tell you this: Tao cannot be told. Being told, it is no longer Tao."

The Master bowed to the students, and they to him, and the gathering was concluded.

# Bird in a Cage,
# Fish in an Aquarium

Teaching martial arts in Asia is a peculiar and complex matter, so mused Master Lam. The entire process of imparting knowledge of the martial arts there in the classic mode is not at all a craft, a trade, or an act of barter. It is rather a way of life. There are no advertisements aimed at recruiting students, nor any bargain for money. Neither incentive nor compulsion is involved. One who might solicit another to become one's student then tacitly bears burdens that would likely impede the pursuit of duty, and such restraint would not be tolerable. That is the way of authentic masters. Yes, Master Lam nodded agreement with himself, students must *search* for authentic masters.

Since the relationship with a master is not a business transaction, the teachings rest freely and totally in the hands of the master. Sometimes teaching proceeds rapidly; at other times teaching is slow, if not leisurely. All depends on the master's mood and on his or her judgment of the progress of the student. Evaluation of that progress is focused basically on the subjective more than on the objective, more on the behavior of the student than on physical ability. Fighting techniques are used simply as tools to serve the global teaching process.

The complementary part of the teaching is often accomplished "off the mat": during break times, tea hour, during a walk in the garden or stroll in the woods. For the more often the students are with the master, the more thoroughly they can absorb the essence of the arts.

Master Lam now considered how best to phrase his words so as best to communicate these truths to the teachers with whom he was now associating. He invited a number of the teachers to join him for a walk in the woods outside Henry's *dojo*.

While strolling and enjoying the beautiful scene and the variety of sweet scents, the myriad colors of blooming flowers here and there, a student observed afar a man hastening toward the group. Master Lam recognized the man immediately. With a smile he hailed the newcomer cheerfully, "Ah, Minh-hai! Minh-hai! What great wind has brought you all the way here? Come, come join us in our stroll."

Minh-hai, a teacher of martial arts who had known Master Lam in their homeland, was one who had come to feel confined within his consciousness, unable to pursue what he believed was the right way and thus unable to bring forth from within him that which he knew was necessary for an authentic relationship with his students.

In his thoughts Minh-hai had recalled again and again the living example of Master Lam. He had re-lived in his mind his participation in a number of seminars with that great teacher and was uplifted simply by remembering the experience. Having heard of Master Lam's visit, Minh-hai decided he must pay his respects to the Master and thus perhaps be helped to discover the way out of his confinement.

The spring morning was warm. Flocks of swallows sang as they soared and swooped, up and down, back and forth in the clear blue sky.

"Listen to the warbling of the birds as they fly. How happy they are!" cried the Master.

"Master," said Minh-hai from out of his analytic mind and at once eager to engage the Master, "you are not a bird. How do you know they are happy?"

Without turning his eyes from the swooping flock, the Master replied, "Minh-hai, you are not I. How do you know I do not know?"

"Well, Master," said Minh-hai, not to be set back lightly, "it is exactly because I am not you that I am not able to know your thoughts. Therefore, whereas you are not a bird, I suppose that you are not able to know the happiness of those birds, or whatever it is they sing. Does my supposition make sense?"

"Wait! Wait just a moment," said the Master, laughing. "Listen to your first question. You asked me how did I know the birds are happy. In asking the question, you accepted that I knew, so you asked me *how* I knew. So I shall tell you how I knew. This is my answer: I look at the swallows soaring and warbling in the clear blue sky, and I know."

Minh-hai lowered his head, kicked small stones with his sandals as he walked, pondered.

Master Lam smiled as he walked, wondering whether Minh-hai was able to relish the repartee as much as the Master did.

"Do you know, Minh-hai, that the dialog between us this morning illustrates two ways of looking at life? On the one hand, the visible world is a reflection of the invisible self, the spirit. I was happy strolling in the pleasant woods in the warmth of the morning, and that pleasure was associated with the soaring birds.

"In this context, your question proceeded from dualistic assumptions about the world, whereas mine emanated from that of the monist who tries always to harmonize his internal self with his surroundings, and whose conception and perception of the world are one and the same.

"On the other hand, this dialog between you and me suggests that we may compare the phenomenon of human life with a mirror. If we smile, it smiles with us; if we weep, it also weeps with us. Figuratively, the mirror reflects our attitude toward life. When we look at life with a gloomy, despondent, pessimistic face, life looks back at us, reflecting our expression. If we wish to change so as to be optimistic, cheerful, buoyant, this change must emanate first from our own consciousness."

"All right, Master," said Minh-hai, casting his gaze upward at the swallows, still darting about in the sky. "How can I be free and happy like those birds up there?"

The Master at once seized the opportunity for which he had been waiting. "Ah! You want to be free, happy, and liberated? Tell me, Minh-hai, who has forced you to live in the cage?"

Minh-hai stopped in his tracks. "Cage? I'm not a caged bird, Master. I'm not living in a cage."

"So, all right, Minh-hai, you are not a bird. Then why do you want to live in the aquarium?"

"Master! I am not a fish, either! I am not living in any aquarium," replied Minh-hai pleasantly, adopting the bantering tone of the Master.

"But, Minh-hai, my friend," said the Master, "you *are* a bird, and not one of those up there." And the Master pointed to the swallows flying free. You are also a fish. For you are confined in the thralldom of rules, regulations, procedures, and directives. Those comprise your cage and your aquarium. Even if they were beautifully, tastefully, expensively decorated with gold filigree and jade and precious gems, your situation would still be the cage and the aquarium.

"Perhaps the cage is not so important to you, but to the people you have sought to please, the appearance of your cage is most important. And your wings, poor bird, are therefore clipped. Can you with wings so clipped remain free? No, your natural disposition is blocked, and you cannot grow in your own natural way. If this situation continues you will wither and die forgotten in darkness, while people continue to worship your cage."

Minh-hai could no longer treat this conversation lightly. It was touching him much too deeply. He forgot the other teachers listening to every word the two spoke. Minh-hai felt his burden keenly. "My wings are clipped, Master. How may I liberate myself from this cage?"

"Minh-hai, you are a martial artist. Of what is the martial arts cage constructed?" Minh-hai shook his head, signifying that he could not answer.

"Let me remind you then, Minh-hai. Is the martial arts cage constructed of belts of various hues signifying technical achievement? Yes. Rank? Yes. Grade? Yes. Authority? Yes. Power? Yes. Abandon such nonsense. These 'construction materials' are superficial, not accomplishment in any way, shape, or form. They are simply ornamental layers of fluff which embellish your outward identity. And that outward identity is a false identity."

The teachers looked at each other in amazement. Some appeared pained by the Master's words.

"And what, Master, is my true identity?" queried Minh-hai.

"It is not something subject to the external world. Rather, it is something that springs from the depths of your being." Master Lam looked compassionately upon the man walking beside him and continued softly, "Awake, Minh-hai! Sing! Jump! Fly! Ah, if only you could. You have been for so long in such a deep sleep. If you do not liberate yourself, then you are no different from the bird in the cage or the fish in the aquarium. If you do not liberate yourself, you will remain a prisoner." Minh-hai again looked puzzled.

Minh-hai thought. "Yes," he said, "I have been imprisoned by those very things you describe, and I came here seeking advice. But," and his voice faltered and became faint, "I had not been aware of the imprisoning features of my life. Thank you, Master."

And Minh-hai bowed deeply to Master Lam, who returned the bow and invited Minh-hai and the group to return to the school and dine. "Let us speak further on this, Minh-hai," said the Master. And the two left the woods and walked back to the school, followed now at a respectful distance by the others who mumbled to each other in puzzlement.

# 11

# HURLING ONESELF AT THE PORTALS OF DEATH

IN OLDEN times masters of the art never imparted their knowledge to students who had not yet reached a certain level of understanding—even if the students were their own sons and daughters. In their teachings they limited their words. To put it more bluntly, they didn't talk much. Master Lam was of that tradition. On the previous day, however, all were amazed to see the Master break with his custom and speak volubly.

It is not difficult to understand why the Master departed from his own tradition, for authentic masters are always abreast of the times. It should be so, for everything in the world keeps moving, changing, transforming. Society changes in response to the push and pull of human emotion and intelligence, and one cannot afford either to stagnate or to follow blindly in the footsteps of others.

For these reasons the Master's advice to Minh-hai was advice to a teacher of advanced training, to a teacher with twenty-five years of experience in guiding students, to a person mature enough to be able to grow on his own once he came to understand the Master's meaning. If the Master's words seemed harsh, his students knew that he was there for them at any time.

The time and subject had been right for Master Lam to seize the opportunity to help Minh-hai solve his problem. Afterwards, he explained, "When the bird has matured to the point that it has feathers are sufficient to keep itself warm, and strong enough to support flight, then the bird flies into the open skies for which it was born. Twenty-five years should be sufficient for Minh-hai's maturity to the point of delivering his valedictory to the fixed forms, rules, and directives of the formal martial art. Those forms and rules are instrumental for the novice and important for the journeyperson, but are only hindrances to the progress of the artist in the advanced stages. Forms and rules are not only hindrances, they are eventually lethal to authentic development."

"Master," inquired Owen, "in your dialog in the woods last week you seemed to imply that the ranking system should be abolished. Why so? If the ranking system is eliminated, how is one to determine one's progress in the training?"

Master Lam replied, "In terms of authenticity, one's progress in martial arts does not proceed from technical performance. Technical performance is in fact peripheral to the more important considerations. The progress of the authentic martial artist is gauged on primordial criteria: the would-be artist's *conduct and evidence of inner growth.*

"These criteria are aimed at preparing the novice for a useful life and a constructive citizenship, as the authentic *do* would have it. The rest—the frantic struggling for colored belts, the fawning over exalted ranks, the constant attention to, and celebration of, technique—these are merely trappings of players in a seriously flawed comedy. Perhaps this comedy is less humorous and more pathetic when we consider again the purpose of the authentic martial artist.

"I used to remind my students to be true to themselves by being honest with themselves, whatever the cost. If that cost be negligible, one might then simply appreciate one's progress. If the cost be great, one must pay it without regret. Only then in the light of clear conscience can one be transformed, can reality manifest itself, and can the cage door fly open and release us.

"'Whatever the cost,' I have said. I mean that in the search for a clean, new, appropriate way to live, one might well hurl oneself at the very portals of death. Did you believe that I was speaking metaphorically? Or was I in fact suggesting that the abolishment of the ranking system in the martial arts is now necessary and appropriate if we are to enter into a new age, a new authentic *do?*

"The act of abolishing rank may be considered the equivalent of hurling oneself at the very portals of death, for today the publicly perceived status and the self esteem of many teachers rests on their right to confer rank. What resentment, suspicion, fear, and general turmoil will be manifested in some practitioners as the base of their status and self-esteem is abandoned! However, built as this status and self-esteem sometimes appears to be on fictions, puffery, show, and general quackery, perhaps the abandonment would be for the best.

"You may recall that once I asked, 'Does the hurricane create unmitigated disaster for people?' and one of you replied at once, 'It certainly does!'

"And I responded, Keep in mind that the disaster is only the action of Tao. It is natural, unstoppable, a harmonious—yes, I repeat harmonious—part of the cosmos. For the violence of the storm here serves to compensate for stagnancy elsewhere. The storm, therefore, helps keep the universe in equilibrium. Might one say, then, that the disaster is 'mitigated'? You may recall that I asked the group to meditate on this truth.

"Just as in nature, when practitioners in art have ventured too far into misdemeanor and thus have insulted art and people, then sooner or later will come a reaction among other practitioners to redress—to balance the misdemeanors. Like the movement of the hurricane which by its nature is unavoidable and unstoppable and aimed at achieving homeostasis, the movement of honest practitioners to balance martial art is natural, appropriate, authentic.

"The movement of microcosm is no different from that of macrocosm. Yes, the abolishment of the ranking system in martial arts would create among a great many professionals a storm of resentment, indignation, anger. One might even quite accurately refer to such a response as 'natural.' The move to non-ranking would be most objected to by those who have plunged most deeply into commercialism.

"Why should this be puzzling when one recognizes that the loss of authority and power would be compensated by the gain of a higher state of consciousness. And this higher state is the putative goal of all those pursuing the *do*. Is it not?

"Those who have set up their goal for the purpose of earning a livelihood are free to choose both goal and livelihood. One hopes those professionals would not delude their students by preaching harmony, love, peace, spirituality. For, as the divine works at a higher level and in more complex dimensions than human words, the professional preaching must be recognized as far less effective than the professional *being* harmonious, loving, peaceful, and spiritual. If I look over my shoulder and appear nervous, it is because I am nervous when I speak to you thus and appear to preach to you." Master Lam laughed but the teacher-students did not.

"Is it not so that preaching must be less effective than being? But shall I continue, in the spirit of paradox?"

"Yes!" all said, now smiling.

"One hears it said that hurling oneself at the gates of death is disrespectful in its unorthodoxy. That the act is, so to speak, un-Tao. But what those who so say are condemning is that which they fear: change and the loss of status.

"The mind of the person who can be identified as 'orthodox' is a mind conditioned by societal tradition, a mind that follows, imitates, copies, steps rigidly in the old patterns. The conditioned mind is an unhealthy mind that identifies as wrong every path other than its own. The orthodox discipline takes the position that it is superior to every other; that it alone follows the perfect path carved out of stone by its master. Well, is there but one path to the summit? Or are there infinite ways?

"The typical path of orthodoxy in any endeavor begins with the founder or innovator establishing a new way—a departure from old ways that is pure and simple in conception and practice and spirit. Over time the innovator passes on, and the heirs uncautiously add and substitute their own interpretations and infuse their own ego needs into the way or the cause. This is done to embellish and decorate and puff the original innovation, often in self-serving ways until the pure spirit of the founding pilgrim is no longer recognizable, and is in fact driven out. Another spirit takes its place, of course—corruption.

"Both leaders and followers in a corrupt organization may have become so immersed in corrupt practices that they are unable to recognize the corruption as such. They do see the conflicts, the hatreds, the rivalries. However, they have taught themselves corrupt new roles. They are like the frog in the pot who does not notice that the water in which he sits is coming to a boil.

"One sees corruption in many organizations—political parties, industries, labor unions, churches, to name a few. One sees corruption in martial arts organizations where both leaders and followers evidently have forgotten the criterion of authenticity and the primacy of the *do*. No need for surprise at this, for life is neither unorthodox nor orthodox. It is mind that makes it either. As the tragic young Danish Prince Hamlet is said to have observed, 'Nothing is either good or bad, but thinking makes it so.'

"But corruption makes for a rough road for novices, idealists, and for those seeking the purity and authenticity for which the true Masters strive. Such persons are often derided as 'unorthodox.' And their response must be merely quiet bemusement—and continued pursuit of the quest.

"Perhaps some of you have identified me as a revolutionary. Well, it may be so. And perhaps one needs revolution when evolution appears to move too slowly or not at all, or when corruption has entered the *do*. Can one be a revolutionary and 'accept all and be at one with Tao?' Of course. Accepting is not a passive state. Doing is not necessarily an active state. As times and circumstances change, so must the teachings. The teachings must change to respond to new realities, but must not sacrifice integrity and must remain consonant with Tao."

"Master," inquired Irving, "according to your exposition it seems that you have made your stand clearly that you cannot be termed a 'perennialist.' We wonder then if you are a pure 'progressive'?"

"The progressive militates for change. The perennialist seeks to ensure that enterprises emphasize the absolute nature and permanence of basic principles. My viewpoint occupies the middle ground. I call for moderation when other voices seek extreme solutions.

"For example, I now suggest to you that awarding grade or rank is not necessarily corrupt or even useless, provided the awarding process is impartial, unprejudiced, and without political coloration. The earning and awarding of grade and rank was once a significant feature in the authentic *do*, in a time when the *do* had not yet plunged into mercantilism. Without discrimination and political prejudices in the awarding process, and including an enhancement of the spiritual factor, grade and rank might regain the integrity it has lost.

"In the process of evaluating a practitioner, evidence of technical ability in the preliminary stages of training is useful, if of secondary importance. Anyone who has ever observed much of the martial arts will recognize that a good technical performer is not necessarily a good person. That unhappy combination of characteristics might be described as an empty container. The empty container floats nicely but, in martial arts as in any other pursuit, does not contribute to balance in the training.

"The good person is not necessarily a good martial arts performer. But the good person—that is, the person who is virtuous in the classical sense that I have defined—who is not a first-rate martial arts performer is already a container with contents, and thus possesses characteristics of mind and heart that help balance the training.

"The school or movement that collects, recognizes, and promotes only facility and ignores virtue becomes a magnet for disturbed practitioners and creates an unhealthy environment that affects the larger society. The society is then burdened with an inclination toward superficiality, and an impatience with ethics and morality.

"I say 'burdened' because the superficial is ephemeral and withers with time. Consider the colored belts that are the delight of so many students today. Think now: Do such belts represent real knowledge? Or do they turn the student's attention away from absorption into the *do*, and instead focus attention on the pomp and ostentation of the award itself, and on the power and fame of the awarding authority.

"As for those awarding authorities who spend their time creating ceremonies and uniforms and badges and belts, how can they teach the authentic *do* when they themselves are in a deep sleep? The worst part is that these authorities present the paper flower as the real thing. They hold it up and sniff at it and sigh with pleasure at its fragrance, and by their example proclaim for students that this is *do*. Does such activity elevate humanity, or only adorn and embellish it in foolish ways?

"But who follows the exploiters? Is it not the unrefined ego, that infant part of the human personality that, untutored, seeks only to gratify itself, and gratify itself in ways it sees others pursue? The ego follows the crowd, imitates the actions of the sheep, bleating the thoughts of those around it. Fearing any disagreement, the ego seeks that which appeases it most effectively, and thus the ego is a ready treat for the exploiter.

"The authentic martial arts teacher recognizes the infant in us, the first phase of the ego. He provides direction and exercise to lead us through the hazards and toward refinement of consciousness—a mature state in which an individual's reasoning becomes important.

"In this second phase of the ego, the individual can become exquisitely aware of the drabness of much conventional thought, can question the existing order with considerable courage, and can assume a thoroughly skeptical view of the world, questioning everything.

"In the third phase of the ego, one passes beyond the restrictions of the ego itself, and begins to harmonize and unify oneself with the unique principle—the universe, the infinity of heaven and earth—to reach the last phase of training which we might refer to as emancipation. In that phase, one is free from external controls and is ready to step *toward the unknown.*

"The unknown, however, by definition is uncharted. Even so, one entering this most mature phase of training might be compared with the crawling baby. For like the infant, the mature martial artist tries to stand and does so for a few seconds before falling down. The baby stands again, and again falls down. And this trial and error continues until a balance is reached and recognized. The mature martial artist, like the baby, walks now, not necessarily surely, but more often than not without wavering. He walks groping the way in the unknown where its egolessness dictates.

"This third phase does not aim toward achievement of a superhuman state, but only to maintain a condition of egolessness. Like the child, the mature martial artist will likely become not only more unpredictable in action, but also illogical in thinking. Action, speech, and writing all become peculiarly different from previous phases. Although the musings of the mature martial artist may appear paradoxical, they are likely to hold truths that ordinary minds find difficult to comprehend.

"'Illogical in thinking,' I said, and so I meant to say. For in order to attain the place which offers the clearest aspect, to see as truly as possible, one must eschew logic and all other forms of reason. One must finally deal in intuition. But the intuition of which I speak is a special phenomenon. It is not that 'sixth sense' of which the popular media make so much, for that particular sense is active only in the area of form and substance.

"The intuition of which I speak embodies great knowledge rather than fragmentary knowledge. It is spiritual intuition that springs from esoteric contemplation rather than from a simple interpretation of the intellect through research in science. This intuition must be apprehended by the heart; it must be lived with, and one must experience life by means of it. Otherwise even this wonderful phenomenon becomes only an entertainment to the brain and contributes nothing beneficial to spiritual life—and of course nothing that would allow one to see into the abiding nature of self."

# 12

# WHO IS
# TO BE BLAMED?

TO MASTER LAM, time seemed to fly by. It had now been more than two months since his arrival in the new land. Near the day that Master Lam had scheduled for his departure, Xuan expressed his desire to return with him to their homeland. This idea was at once disapproved by both Hau and Master Lam, on grounds that the homeland still Lay in chaos and now needed only qualified technicians and specialists in various fields. Master Lam and Hau advised Xuan to stay and pursue an advanced academic degree.

Thinking of ways to make his own visit more fruitful, and knowing that back home the resourceful Totu would responsibly carry on the activities of the school, Master Lam decided to extend his visit in order to further instruct Xuan, Henry, An-nan, and the other listeners. He then taught the essentials of health-preservation, holistic healing, and the importance of sowing the right seeds in the field of martial arts so as to benefit the younger generations—the future custodians of the martial arts. This last point Master Lam considered to be vital.

During the first of several final gatherings, Master Lam made a special request of the teachers. He asked them to pay close attention to the teaching of youth. "From my reading," he said, "and from my viewing of television, and my personal observation, I have come to sad conclusion about the situation in which a great many young persons find themselves today. It is a state of confusion. A large proportion of them are without role models and guides."

Some of the young people with whom Master Lam had spoken referred to the general "busyness" of their parents and the scarcity of conversation or the sharing of meals with them. Others described their misery as a result of parental separation or divorce. Still others admitted that their parents were continuing victims of alcohol or drug abuse. Some, from whose attitudes and behavior Master Lam felt might be especially troubled, felt and said that they has "no problem." This was a phrase that Master Lam heard time and again, especially from those young people whose behavior, every adult agreed, seemed distinctly troubling.

The senior Roland remarked, "Many of our people have aspirations for scholarship, but they are bored with ethics. They wish to amass material things, and are not concerned about gaining wisdom. Throughout our society we teach about rights, but we very often neglect teaching about responsibilities, probably fearful of appearing to 'preach.' Master, do you suppose such things are root causes of our losing so many young people to vice, sloth, and carelessness?"

The Master recognized that he was a guest in the country and was not eager to speak out in criticism, but felt obligated to speak the truth as he saw it. He therefore answered, "In any society, especially an industrialized one, wherein the people are concerned more for comfort, pleasure, and wealth than with ethics and wisdom, they are likely to neglect and ignore the needs of their children. Whereas such people may provide food, shelter, and clothing for their offspring, they may not consider as at all important the foundation of human character that is constructed and strengthened in the home, and nowhere else. If parents fail in this part of their duty—the proper instilling in the young of respect, discipline, and regard for the persons and property of others—then they are only sowing the seeds of their children's destruction."

Christiane looked pained and said, "I am hesitant to lay blame on parents. I'm a parent myself and I never had any training in how to do it—how to be a parent, I mean. Also, my parent's weren't the best models, I guess. As long as we kids kept out of their hair, they didn't pay much attention to us. When I even thought about the future, what I saw for myself was insecure and dim. I guess many of my friends had the same experience."

Encouraged by this painfully honest unburdening, Roland observed, "It seems to me that our whole society has come off track. Now, what's the best way to get back on track? Is it at all helpful just to blame our parents, or 'society'? Maybe there is something that we as martial arts teachers can do to remedy some of this untidy condition. What do you think, Master?"

All eyes were on Master Lam. "Well," he said, "there is always the possibility." He smiled. "Knowing to scratch were it itches is the objective." Master Lam paused for a few seconds and said, "The more we penetrate into this problem, the more we are likely to see parents as blameworthy. However, we must try to understand that parents, too, have been brought up by parents.

"If, indeed, society is in this awful condition, then we can do nothing, unless each one of us dares to start a revolution—a radical revolt in consciousness, I mean."

"How are we to go about doing that, Master?" asked Roland.

"One must first discipline oneself," replied the Master, casting a glance at Xuan and seeing him smile softly as he recognized a saying the Master had repeated time and again throughout Xuan's early training. "I believe that self-discipline is the key to the problem. If each of us becomes able to restrain evil cravings, get rid of excessive greed and selfishness, overcome a good deal of our ignorance about how a good society should work, then much of the problem will begin to resolve itself. I used the phrase *evil cravings* advisedly, for I believe that one must first recognize that some cravings are inimical not only to the welfare of the individual, but to society as well. We must return to broad agreement about what is desirable behavior; and as individuals, and as a society, we must not be tolerant of globally undesirable attitudes and behavior.

"I understand that it has become fashionable for some men to justify their thievery, violence, use of humanity-degrading language, sexual and civic irresponsibility, and sloth on grounds that some manufactured 'cultural norm' expects or requires such behavior. That position is dishonest and intolerable. The truth is that no surviving social group in all of history has espoused such personally and socially lethal behaviors. Whatever one's 'culture,' be it ethnic or racial or manufactured ad hoc, one does not have the right to act in ways damaging to the greater society."

"So, Master, where do we begin?" Roland insisted.

The Master smiled. "So, let us begin at the beginning. As nearly everyone must know, early childhood is the critical phase in learning. Children mimic their elders. The behavior that parents model governs the habits of their children and is engraved in their consciousness—and in their subconscious. So, if one becomes a parent, one is obligated to practice self-discipline in order to provide a decent model for the offspring. Should you not desire to provide such a model, then do not become a parent."

Master Lam paused. "Of course, it is easy to say such things. What if, as is so often the case, men and women—and now, more often, boys and girls—produce children carelessly, offhandedly, thoughtlessly, heedlessly, and then recognize no obligation nor bother to serve as decent role models? Then what is to happen?" Master Lam looked about the group and asked again, "After parents, who are those who are most influential in the lives of children?"

"Ah," said one. "Teachers."

"Exactly, teachers," agreed Master Lam. "By definition, teachers are supposed to be living examples and reinforce right and proper behavior in children. That is what we do, and who we are. That is our commitment."

"Well, Master," said Roland. "Should this commitment be taken over from incompetent parents by others, such as the state, for example?"

"I will say this: Even as you must train to be a teacher, even as you must spend much time and energy learning your art and learning how to teach, so any parent must 'train' to be a parent and learn how to fulfill those obligations. And if children are produced by those who have no training, no feeling of obligation, no art, then teachers—whether in governmental or civilian institutions—must do the job.

"Now, if the mirrors of honesty, generosity, and morality are begrimed, that is, if the teachers themselves are corrupted, then even the most beautiful soul among children has much less chance of becoming an honest, generous, and morally straight adult."

Evidently annoyed, Donald spoke up again. "This miserable situation we are facing today, this corruption of society and the loss of generations, has been created by politicians who take our tax money and spend it on all kinds of programs, projects, and strategies for youth that don't produce a thing. Things don't get better; they just get worse." The speaker looked about the room then at Master Lam, perhaps seeking confirmation for his point of view.

Master Lam said, "Are you addressing me?"

"Ah, well, yes, Master. Well, I guess . . . Forgive me, please, for bringing up a point that, I guess, doesn't much relate to our field of martial arts."

Master Lam was thoughtful and silent for a long moment, then replied: "I think your point does relate to our field. I must admit that I do not know and understand thoroughly how your governmental system works in all its complex parts. I do believe that, whatever the system of government, elected and appointed authorities have an obligation to deal with the causes of the diseases of society, not simply patch over the wounds.

"There are many ways to approach a disease. If the disease affects children, perhaps the most constructive beginning is for us to agree that, although there may be an occasional statistical exception, children are not born bad. Such behavior is learned. If they are deprived of affirmative models, if they are left to drift and follow only personal pleasure, they are likely to become troubled and troubling. Can we agree on that?" The teachers nodded in agreement.

"Let me pursue the agreement botanically. A plant whose leaves are being eaten by insects may not need a dose of insecticide. Perhaps what it really needs is the right fertilizer. A tree whose growth is stunted may require more watering or it may need to be removed entirely. And perhaps that tree should have been more carefully tended to when it was a seedling." There were more nods of agreement from the teachers.

"So, too," continued Master Lam, "in working with young human beings we shall be more successful if we deal in prevention, and not 'cure.' Prevent their straying from the path, reward their staying on the path. Above all, pay attention to them and care about and for them. Prevention is the natural way. The 'cure,' if it works at all, will take a very long time."

Casey wondered, "'A very long time' for a cure, you say, Master. How long is that?"

"Possibly generations," replied Master Lam.

At that the teachers were discomfited, their mouths gaped. They looked at each other, shaking their heads as if discouraged at the Master's words.

"Generations!" repeated one teacher quietly.

"I said 'possibly generations,'" said Master Lam, "for as you have described it, the society is seriously diseased. We must not 'remove' the 'diseased' children as we 'remove' the stunted tree. We must do all we can to relieve their pain and go to the root causes of the disease. Our primary task, then, is to educate the children in appropriate behavior during their earliest and most impressionable years.

"I say 'educate' but I also mean 'indoctrinate.' If we are able to agree on expectations for right and proper behavior, we can adopt a common *doctrine* for what is 'good.' The time for agreeing and doing is now. Others may envision problems arising from trying to find agreement among many different points of view, and I agree that finding common ground in politics is sometimes difficult. But in identifying proper behavior in our children, I foresee no major 'cultural' hindrances, no real disputes among parents and teachers from different racial and ethnic groups. Then, of course, as teachers we must have the will and the perseverance to attend to the reinforcements of the proper behavior as paramount among our many priorities. We must also demonstrate the leadership necessary to do this important job."

"Master," asked Donald, "what about self-esteem and teaching the basics and so on? Should those things be important teaching priorities?"

"Certainly," replied Master Lam. "One cannot teach only 'behavior' and get the job done. What I have said, and will say again, is that without long-term and consistent teaching of the tenets of proper behavior, as agreed upon by the larger society—leadership again—our little 'trees' will wither and be stunted or die. I remind you that it must be 'long-term and consistent' teaching because of the general impatience apparent in society. It seems that people want things done in short order, 'now.' They want bad things fixed, 'right now.' I would only remind those people that broken bones do not mend 'right now,' and that mending the ills of society will require a long-term and continuing commitment."

The clock struck twelve, and Master Lam recognized a weariness of mind in the expressions of the teachers. He decided to conclude the meeting with the following words: "Human society is made by people, people like us. We are its designers and builders. When the structure of society is right, we all benefit. When the structure is not right, we are bound to suffer. A human problem is solvable by humans. We have option to either change or remain as we are. Is the task difficult? Yes, but not insuperably so. Remember the old saying: 'The difficult is easier for those who set their minds to the task.'"

# 13

# THE LAST HOMILY OF MASTER LAM

THE TEACHERS had gathered for their final meeting with Master Lam, for he had decided that it was time for him to return to his native land. The dozen or so teachers were seated in a semicircle in the courtyard enjoying the pleasant weather and looking forward to more of Master Lam's teaching which, they all agreed, had stimulated their thinking enormously.

"Master," said Donald who was always concerned with ethical matters at the beginning of the session, "in your earlier remarks you have sometimes used the word 'master' to designate teacher, and sometimes 'teacher' to designate master. Is there a difference in meaning of these terms? And what of the term 'instructor'?

"I am very glad you have asked this question," said Master Lam. "Since arriving in this country I have come to realize that in the West you often use these terms

synonymously, and I have just become Westernized."
All chuckled at this, and the Master continued. "In
Western university life, instructor is an academic rank
on the way to becoming a professor. The instructor may
be remarkably knowledgeable in the field and require
only the passage of time until the highest status is
achieved. But in martial arts there is a profound and
functional difference in the meaning of the terms.

"In the culture of martial arts as practiced in the East,
the instructor is one who learns a skill and transfers that
learning to others, usually without necessarily understanding its philosophy or meaning. The instructor has
learned by rote and repetition, teaches by rote and repetition, and expects students to learn by rote and repetition. He or she is able to demonstrate technique and
is considered a trainer—an apprentice teacher—who
possess a specific, limited body of knowledge.

"Nowadays, those qualified only to be instructors very
often commonly refer to themselves as teachers. As a
result of these abuses of terminology, there is no clear
delineation of status. Unfortunately, some of these people—instructors, I mean—may also be charismatic,
charming charlatans who may be more attractive to the
masses than are the masters. They are able to present a
childish logic—such as we use when we note that nine
minus two equals seven, for example—and convince
people to believe that this is authentic martial arts philosophy. It is possible for the ignorant and gullible to
follow such people and believe they are 'learning martial arts.'"

"Master," cried Casey, "I am confused. 'Nine minus two equals seven' seems very logical to me, and probably to everyone here today, and maybe to all the world. How is such logic not fit for martial arts?"

"A fine question," replied Master Lam. "Let me tell you a story. Once I asked my two nephews, ages six and seven, if they knew how to do subtraction and addition. 'Yes, Uncle,' they said. Then I said, 'Look at the electric wire above you. Can you count the number of birds perching on that wire?' Both counted and answered, 'Nine birds.'

"'Very good,' I said, 'Suppose I use a gun and shoot and kill two of those. You say you know how to do subtraction. So now I ask you, how many birds are left on the wire?' The boys counted with their fingers and proudly answered, 'Seven!' And I—not using the latest in instructional techniques—replied, 'Wrong!' The six-year-old looked at me perplexed and said, 'Uncle, you just don't know how to do subtraction.' His brother laughed. I laughed." Master Lam looked at Xuan, who had remained in the same kneeling position for a long time. "Xuan," said Master Lam, "How could I have explained why my little nephews were incorrect?"

"Well, Master," replied Xuan. "First, they couldn't understand the reason for your declaring their answer 'wrong'. I think I would try to clarify that, by explaining that the detonation of the gun scared the birds and caused them to fly away, and so that was the reason none was left on the wire. I believe they would then understand."

Master Lam nodded his head and smiled at Xuan.

"Of course, of course. And my nephew's answer was 'right' as well as incorrect; 'logical' as well as wrong. Nine minus two does equal seven. However, reality does not conform with general belief, else we should all believe that the world is flat, as it appears to be. Reality has to do with evidence, facts that exist independent of reason. There is nothing wrong with the reasoning of children—they have their various stages of development, and they are practicing finding answers to the mysteries of the world. No, there is nothing wrong with the reasoning of children—unless it is employed by adults and passed off as mature reasoning.

"You might say that I tricked my nephews. I would reply that in the real world circumstances sometimes bristle with snares and traps, and that the thinking process of adults is characterized by an awareness of intricacy, complexity, subtlety. Yes, of course, there are degrees of those qualities invested in all of us, and as we mature we expect to grow in each. In adult life, we might conclude that very often nine minus two equals eighty-two or fourteen—sometimes, it even equals zero!

"Childish-minded teaching has a general appeal, for it requires nothing but the emulation of demonstrated skills. Childish-minded teaching remains at the surface. Unfortunately, a great many teachers nowadays fall into this childish mode. They invest in pleasantness, in feel-good-ness, a temporary entertainment of the senses. They slap students on the back indiscriminately and say, 'good' and 'well done' and they present 'best student of the lesson' awards. And students come to expect to be praised, whatever their achievement. It seems that some may be thinking, 'Tell me I'm good, even if you have to lie.' I say to you, be aware that in this life there is the reproach that praises, and the praise that reproaches.

"A paradoxical corollary to teaching in the childish mode is teaching from the head rather than from the heart. Please understand this: Teaching from the head closes off a variety of options for the students."

The young teacher Gary asked, "Master, what do you mean by 'praise that reproaches'?"

The Master answered, "One superb gift a teacher can provide a student is the freedom to act. The routine awarding of praise can train the student to respond in ways that are limited by the teacher's own limitations."

The Master paused and asked if any member of the group had comment regarding his exposition. Xuan remained in his kneeling position, his eyes and lips smiling as if he were unable to alter that expression of complete satisfaction. No one offered a question or a comment. All seemed deep in thought.

"All right, to get back to the original question," the Master said, "I will say that in the Western tradition a *Master* is 'one who is eminently skilled in an occupation, art, science.' I must also say that it may be that the focus in the Western tradition is on the objective side of the equation.

"In the Eastern tradition, a Master lives on both sides of the equation and beyond, but never ever claims to be a master. The self-proclaimed master is not only a contradiction in terms, but also considered to be ridiculous and pathetic—the term *Master* is an honorary title bestowed by others who make the judgment based on the subject's personality, conduct, deeds, life experience, and so forth."

Yvonne observed, "I hate to tell you this, Master, but I know of a young man around here, age about twenty, who advertises himself 'Master' So-and-So. He has a lot of students and makes a lot of money. We laugh at his presumption, but we're well aware that he's not the only one." Yvonne paused and looked around. "Perhaps we ought to take time to scrutinize all the masters we've known, and examine what we know of their teaching and their lives, and try to figure out if they deserve to be known as Masters, those to whom we as sincere students might surrender our hearts and souls."

The Master nodded, smiling. "Perhaps such an effort would be a help in re-directing your pursuit of your art. Keep in mind that the authentic master is a nobody who lives on a very personal plane of being, without bragging about personal accomplishment or achievement. The authentic master evidences no personal concern whether addressed as 'Master' or as 'Hey,' for both terms are artistically meaningless. The Master is exempt from such criticism, living with clear conscience, in equanimity with all, and often in anonymity."

"Master, you said 'a nobody'?" inquired Yvonne again. "Really?"

"Authenticity resides in the process of becoming authentic. By the time he or she becomes known, the master and the mastery are often misunderstood. People generally want to see in the Master something extraordinary, something grand, something astounding. But the more conspicuous the master, the smaller the master becomes in the eyes of the people who, after all, are seeing with eyes not educated in martial arts.

"I did say 'nobody'. Become a 'nobody,' yes. To become a nobody is not easy. It is surely not a life for the egotist!" The Master reminded the group that his master, Tai-Anh, daily worked within himself to be able to inspire in others that inner growth and development, to bring others to their level of attained consciousness. Before Master Tai-Anh went into seclusion, he lived simply. He did not really teach, he demonstrated, for his daily living was a demonstration. He was free from the fever of social display, and thus remained simple and clean, devoid of all luxury.

"But people do not at once see that path, the path that constitutes the process of authenticity. All ask for direction to that path, but many never see it. 'Where is the path?' they ask. The Master never shows the path, but only furnishes the light by which one may come to see. As each individual is different, each must find the path separately. The false master shows you the path and requires that you follow directives.

"The authentic Master understands that self-knowledge is the first step toward self-realization. On this spiritual plane the Master requires no certification or authority or testament. Realization is quite enough, and experience is self-proof. But then, be advised, there is a worldly penalty: In the eyes of the many, of those whose 'logic' is the straightforward logic of the child, the Master's behavior is likely considered odd, eccentric. And oddness, eccentricity, may result in condemnation by the many."

"Oh, my!" exclaimed Casey, looking bewildered and thereby expressing the feeling of many in the group.

"Only listen to this," said Master Lam: "There once was a teacher of martial arts who had spent a major part of his life in search of an authentic master. He had met many teachers—including as might be expected, a few who proclaimed themselves 'master'—but none exhibited the qualities that might satisfy the criterion. One morning the teacher stopped at an inn to have a cup of tea and met an old man who showed him the way to find a real master. The elder simply advised: 'According to your narrative, the one you are searching for would be the most ordinary person. Yes, the most ordinary person, remember!'

"After three more years of searching in vain for such a 'most ordinary person,' the teacher returned to his community and again met the old man. The teacher complained, 'It's been almost three years that I have been searching for that most ordinary person you advised me to look for, but I couldn't find one.'

"The old man replied, 'Well, it is obvious that you have been looking in all the high-visibility places, visiting the greatest *dojos*, enrolling in the best-known schools. In such places you can find only extraordinary persons, exceptional masters, well-known from glamorous advertisements, persons with high rank and hundreds of followers. How could you find there that most ordinary person you seek? I say once again that the person you seek will be unresponsive to the seductions of this world.'

"'Well, how about a few hints?' prompted the man. 'The well-known masters are right there, a lot of them on the market. How in the world should I go about finding the unknown? I mean, this ordinary person is difficult to find. Please steer me in the right direction with maybe a few hints or clues.'

"'Hints? Clues?' retorted the old man. Without further words he flicked the sleeve of his robe at the teacher's face. Although the flicked sleeve did not reach the teacher's face, the current of a mysterious force from the act was so powerful that the teacher was pushed backward and thrown to the floor. As the teacher struggled to arise he received yet another flick and was knocked to the floor again, while the old man sat quietly savoring his tea, his composure distinguished, serene, as if nothing unusual had happened.

"The teacher was awestruck. He suddenly realized that the most ordinary person for whom he had been searching was not far away, but right before him. He rose to his knees and begged the old man to be his master.

"'If you want to learn more, then go to the well-known masters, those who have many followers. Go to all the seminars. Go to the workshops. Get promoted to higher ranks. If you become my student you will earn disappointment and frustration. You will learn not a single thing from me, for I teach only unlearning, the unrememberable, the forgettable. Besides, I will try to take away from you every technique you have, until you have nothing left in your mind.'

"The teacher remained on his knees and vowed to surrender himself unconditionally to the elder's eccentricity. He had heard a truth in the absurdity and mystery of the elder's response, a truth not logical, not rational at all, but a perceived truth nevertheless."

Master Lam looked about the room and saw manifested among his listeners interest, confusion, frustration, perplexity, irritation, and resignation. "Shall I continue?" asked Master Lam.

"Yes, Master, please do," was the reply from the group.

"As you might have imagined, the teacher-supplicant became a novice again and served the old Master for a number of years. One morning while dusting a table he dropped a flower vase. The vase broke into pieces as it hit the floor. Without warning, the ancient Master launched a punch at his student's face, and persisted in an attack that required the student first to resist with all his might and then, when the Master's attack did not diminish, to fight back. In fighting back, the student did not think about what he was doing; he did not consider the relationship that had grown ever more intimate with the Master. The student now wanted only to remove himself from a situation that had become a danger to his own well-being.

"The Master suddenly ended the combat by striking his disciple on the back with a finger. The student felt a tingling sensation running along his body; he sank to the floor. Walking away, the Master said, 'Now go away. You may return when I am no longer on earth. Go now!'

"Lying on the floor, the disciple saw crumble that Master-disciple relationship which he had treasured and thought so beautiful and so sustaining. He arose, gathered his few belongings, and departed."

Master Lam sat for some moments in silence. Finally, Yvonne spoke up. "Master, what happened then?"

"Ah, you wish to know what happened. Well, after many years the disciple learned that his Master had recently died, and he made haste to return for the memorial ceremony. People regarded him curiously. A man of middle age said, 'We know that the Master dismissed you, threw you out. How is it that you return?'

"'The day he threw me out, my beloved Master said that I could return when he is no longer on earth. That day has come. Here I am. I obey him. I am his disciple, and he is my Master.'

"'I don't understand,' said the man.

"'Yes, that is obvious,' replied the disciple, a man now with respectful students of his own. 'But your ignorance is innocent and it will moderate in time. For now, know that the Master's hard shell contained a deep compassion and that, had he not dismissed me, I should never have learned what I have learned, never would have known what I now understand. Yes, I suffered deeply, I wept. But then my anger and pain and disappointment disappeared. I regained my clarity through hours of meditation. And while I was left in that tranquillity and aloneness I perceived something, a flash of intuition, and I came to realize that his throwing me out had awakened me. The Master had created a pretext, the broken vase, for dismissing me in that eccentric way that authentic masters so often follow.

"'You will say, Why use lethal techniques against a faithful disciple, especially as the Master was the superior in technique? And I answer, His action was only a test to ascertain my readiness to leave him. I passed that test. Throwing me out was the only way left that he felt he could help me. Can you understand that?'"

Master Lam ended his story, and the session, by reviewing some of the precepts he had earlier presented. "Remember that finding a 'master' nowadays is not difficult at all. They seem to be everywhere—celebrating themselves on posters, in movies, on television programs. But those ordinary persons I told you about, the real Masters, the authentic Masters, are more difficult to find. Those who have nothing inside inevitably brag about their superiority, the superiority of their technique, the supremacy of their school, the glory of their rank. Keep in mind that superiority is always claimed by the inferior.

"It did not take talking or bragging or striking with an ax for the old Master to communicate the truth to his disciple. It took a single flick of his sleeve. And in casting his disciple into the world the Master demonstrated the true martial arts—alpha and omega and all between.

# 14

## FAREWELL AND A NEW BEGINNING

ON THE AFTERNOON of Master Lam's departure, the members of the school bade him farewell, and returned directly from the airport to Henry's school for what Henry termed a "wrap-up." Each remarked on the ways they had been affected by Master Lam's teachings and touched by his very presence. Although the Master was no longer present in the flesh, he had left behind some of his spirit, a profound impression of harmony and unity. The teachers felt a genuine and beautiful rapprochement developing among themselves.

Recognizing the unifying force of Master Lam's influence, they decided without discussion that they would continue to strengthen their relationship with one another, and their individual resolve to "make a difference" by reviewing the Master's essential message.

Christiane spoke up. "I have spent the last twenty

years in martial arts," she said. "For the last five years something, perhaps intuition, has told me that there is a higher goal than that to which I then aspired, a goal better than accumulating technique and grade. I have gone to seminars and classes far and wide searching for that 'something.' I never found it until now. I believe I have found it in the teachings of Master Lam."

The other teachers agreed. "But haven't you learned something new in each of the 'far-and-wide seminars'?" asked Gordon.

"Yes, of course," replied Christiane, "but I now believe that such learning is trivial compared with the insights I have gained here in the last few weeks." She looked about the group. "Does anyone disagree?"

Xuan smiled.

"I agree with you," said Henry, "but maybe you could describe your understanding of your recent learning, and maybe that would help us sort out our own gains."

"All right. I'll try," Christiane replied, shifting her posture so as to be more comfortable. "Do you agree that most martial arts practitioners and even leaders we know are not at all conversant with 'spirituality' as it relates to martial art?" The teachers nodded in agreement. "It is true, is it not, that many appear uncomprehending or even alarmed when they are confronted with that word—spirituality—in connection with martial arts?

The company nodded again and Christiane pursued her point. "As Master Lam mentioned the other day, spirituality is not something disconnected from our being, but permeates the whole being. It is not something exceeding humankind, but it is rather a *fragrance* of humankind. If we are really human, so we are also spiritual."

She continued, "I have come to be aware that many, if not most, people enter martial arts training for what we have recently learned are the 'wrong reasons.' For example, they want to gain some immediate physical advantage over their peers. Or they want to experience confidence. As motives these are innocent enough, I suppose, and certainly understandable in light of the media exposure of martial arts. But I had been unable to identify the major problem, the problem that Master Lam has helped me understand, the problem that we can help solve."

"I think we know what you're about to say," said Henry, smiling and looking about the group, "but please articulate that problem for us!"

Christiane continued, "The problem is in the teaching, of course. But not only the act of teaching and its objectives, but more importantly, the motivations for teaching." She paused, considering how to frame her question. "As teachers, do we teach so as to help our students transform themselves, or do we teach to gain and consolidate our own authority over our students?"

Henry replied, "We know what we ought to do."

Christiane nodded in agreement. "We know what we ought to do *if* we have been enlightened to our purpose as teachers."

"Master Lam has brought us that enlightenment. He

came here to initiate our first steps in transformation to the unknown. His perspective is what I have been longing for, what I have searched for all these years."

"I, too, feel that," offered the much older teacher Roland, a fifty-year practitioner of martial arts.

"Speaking frankly," continued Christiane, "as I shall do now and forever more," she added, smiling broadly, "seminars and workshops are usually fun." All agreed. "But they are also part of that questionable struggle for advancement, for promotion in grade."

"Yes," said Henry. "If the exercise and the general fun in learning were all that martial art is concerned with, then we could enjoy those parts and leave it at that."

"However," continued Christiane, "the ranking and grading hypnotizes the novices. They then become drawn into the vicious higher circles of competition for authority where conflict, hostility, enmity are most likely to flourish." She looked about the group and saw in every face the recognition of the truth she was enunciating.

"Master Lam identified that problem in several different ways, didn't he," remarked Roland. "He also pointed out several times in several different ways how varied life is, how sudden its changes are, and how all human experiences—foolish but sublime, repulsive but attractive, painful but ecstatic—are part of the same fabric: life. By that I believe he means that we shouldn't spend our lives bemoaning life's ills, but rather take whatever steps are available to celebrate life's beauty and good, and do something to remedy its ills."

"Even if it's painful to do," said the younger teacher Gary.

"As we always say, 'no pain, no gain,'" responded Roland, to the laughter of the group. "Christiane has implied that her life had a large empty place in it until recently. I have to confess that I have been asleep for far too long." He looked down at his folded hands and mused. "I regret that I did not meet Master Lam long ago." He smiled. "But as we also say, 'better late than never.'" All chuckled.

Now Owen spoke up. "It seems that many of us here, perhaps all of us? have had the same experience: Running after popular teachers, striving for rank and, I guess, 'fame.' How embarrassing now to see myself in that light! Now that I know what I know." He looked at another teacher, Craig. "I stopped the other day and watched Craig here, and I couldn't identify any of the conventional patterns, but his movements were marvelously effective, beautiful. I asked him after class how he had arrived at those movements, and he said he didn't know what I was talking about."

Craig smiled and shook his head. "I think now that maybe for a time I'd passed over that barrier Master Lam referred to and gone into another dimension. Sounds pretentious to say so, but I do think that's what happened."

Owen nodded in agreement. "I think so, too." His eyes twinkled. "Well," he said, "now that we have all this baggage, shall we create our own system? Could we call it maybe the Master Lam System?"

Xuan said, "Or the Master Lam Non-System?"

Recognizing Owen's and Xuan's proposals as extensions of their usual, sophisticated humor, Craig countered with, "How about the 'Nameless System'?"

"Yes, quite correct!" came the response from several.

Christiane reminded the group, "Recall Master Lam's quotation of Lao-tsu: 'The name that can be named is not the eternal name.'" All clapped in appreciative applause.

"Well," said Burt, a much younger teacher, "I'm not at the level of the rest of you, so a bunch of these things still confuse me. Can anybody tell me where that *right path* is? Is there a special one? And also, if rank and promotions don't really mean anything in martial arts, then how do we recognize achievement—if we are to recognize achievement?"

The questioner looked at Henry, but Henry turned to Xuan as if for help. Xuan had been sitting silent in the circle of participants throughout the conference, silent but with a smile on his face. With confidence and with his smile broadening Xuan responded, "Master Lam once said that one is on the right path of training when an inner transformation has overtaken the outer training."

Burt looked blank, and Xuan continued, "At a certain level in our training we must transcend our techniques. If we continue imitating others—performing prescriptions—we will not only reach nowhere, but we will become lost. In that loss we will resort to showing off our rank, title, and so forth, in order to prove our achievement to anyone who might be impressed by that sort of thing." Xuan observed that Burt was listening carefully. He pursued, "You recall that Master Lam often emphasized that achievement relates to reality, not to appearance. For that reason Master Lam's attempt for the last two months was not to furnish us with more and newer technical know-how, but rather to show us the way to grasp the salient points that will move us toward our inner light. *The inner light will illumine our path.* That's the path you're talking about, and that path is different for each individual, although its end is the same for all."

Casey observed, "I understand that real achievement is concerned with being, rather than with appearance. But didn't Master Lam also say once that appearance is important?"

Xuan then tried to clarify this point. "Master Lam may have implied in one or another context that he is not opposed to appearance, but that is not to say he is *for* appearance!" Casey scowled in puzzlement, and Xuan continued. "When Master Lam said that techniques of fighting are important, he was stating the obvious, but he was using a word that is tricky because it has several meanings. Take that statement of Master Lam to mean that the word *appearance* in this context means the coming forth—that techniques must originate from within and come forth unbidden, not be called forth.

"One practices and practices technique after technique, in all manner of forms and under different circumstances to the point at which one is totally practicing and not at all conscious of one's practice. One uses the techniques to delve deeper and deeper into the totality. Then in that totality one may discover the beyond and drop all awareness of technique. Both the dropping and the awareness are unconscious acts.

"But most practitioners do not understand this truth, probably have never considered its possibility, very likely have never been taught anything like it, sad to say. For most practitioners evidently are satisfied with the layers of appearance they have acquired, with technique they have performed to the applause of all. They enjoy the feeling, but of course it is not lasting nor is it of value artistically and spiritually.

"Master Lam used to say to us novices that if one can delve deeply enough into the beyond, one will reach the divine and partake of the everlasting. At that depth one requires a different quality of vision, for ordinary eyes can see only the finite. But of course the divine is always with us. It requires only one's diligent attention to the spiritual, a quality that the pursuit of belt, rank, grade, fame very effectively blots out."

The teachers were delighted with Xuan's knowledge and especially with his clear exposition of Master Lam's spirit. They regarded him with evident respect.

"I wonder," said Yvonne to the members of the group, "has Master Lam incorporated other systems into one? It seems to me that his style of movement embraces all the different systems I'm aware of."

"I believe I can respond to that," said Henry, "Master Lam has said that when he was young he learned different arts, and that each art has its own characteristics, peculiarities, and qualities. At the elementary stages of any art its differences from other arts is clear. But the deeper one delves into one art, the nearer one feels the similarity with others. There is a subtle harmony in them, because all authentic arts spring from the same source. Whatever the style, the diligent searcher can reach the same center, for each of us has that potential."

"Yes! I have experienced that feeling of similarity," cried Owen. "My performance toward the end of the second month was almost an 'out-of-body' feeling. I seemed to have accidentally touched some force out of myself. While engaged in combat I didn't remember any 'form' or any 'technique' at all. My consciousness was in a state of flux and I felt an energy within me I'd never before experienced." Owen had become animated, his face glowing, his eyes bright. He took a breath and shouted, "Eureka! I am in emptiness!" He looked about at the other members of the group. "You are in nothingness, too. Now we know nothing!" And he laughed, and the others took up the laughter and the hall rang with their joy.

"Teacher An-nan!" called Henry.

All turned to An-nan who had sat immobile, eyes closed. Every now and then he had nodded as if dozing. Occasionally a small smile flitted across his face as if he were enjoying one or another idea going by in his head. Apparently he had been uninterested in the discussion.

An-nan opened his red-rimmed eyes. "Hah," he responded.

"Have you something to share with us? All of us would like to hear from you," said Henry.

"Me? Share, Mr. Henry?" An-nan appeared confused.

"We are trying to gather together Master Lam's essential teaching, and we would like to hear your suggestions," repeated Henry.

An-nan said, "I appreciated your discussion, my friends. But 'share'? No, my joy is beyond expression; therefore, I am unable to 'share.' Frankly, I don't know how to verbalize it. Be assured, though, that I am saturated with every word that has passed your lips today. My silence is not negative; it is part of a flowering that has been taking place within me. Several times during your comments I have savored points that were new to me, and I have been selfishly relishing those beauties."

"Would you share some of those beauties with us?" asked Yvonne, curious.

An-nan sat with his mouth open, his expression again blank, at a loss as to how to express his feeling in words. "How can I share my feelings? I don't know that it is possible to do that, and I certainly can not. I could share my knowledge, but of course, as Master Lam has reminded us, knowledge is not at all knowing, which is part of being.

"If I'm not mistaken, Master Lam's intention was not with appearance, with our ability to perform techniques. He was concerned with our being. He pushed us to leap into our inner being and then beyond our self-imposed limitations. So, I can share my knowledge. That's not so difficult. Books and video tapes can display knowledge in this way. Teachers and masters can communicate knowledge in this way. Priests and monks, too, can transfer their knowledge by preaching. But all this is still only knowledge, not knowing. I have realized that the knowledge I have accumulated for so many years is actually of no use to my inner being.

"With all my knowledge, I can be a high-ranking black belt or a no-ranking beginner. I remain the same me until I make the leap into the inner world." An-nan had spoken in a straight tone, quietly. He then closed his eyes as if he were looking inward. It appeared that some sort of inspiration had touched him. Opening his eyes he pursued, "I don't know how I have come to these conclusions; they simply appeared to me. I apologize for lecturing to you. I have no business lecturing to anyone."

All were struck with such powerful words emanating from a man who had recently appeared so thoughtless, so rude, so strange. And now he had brought all his thinking into an inspired focus and touched them all.

Henry spoke for the group. "No, Teacher An-nan," he said, "we'd like to hear more from you. Please don't stop now!"

An-nan hesitated only a moment. With a self-deprecating smile, he continued, "That 'knowledge' I just mentioned is poisonous, you know. It has just about killed me. It made my life miserable, set me between life and death." Suddenly, An-nan turned toward Xuan and bowed formally to him, an act that the group found almost bizarre, and certainly unexpected.

"'Knowledge!'" An-nan continued in low and measured tones. "'Knowledge!' I keep repeating this word because it reminds me of a most unsavory incident in my past. I must confess. Twelve years ago I came to a school of martial arts and was greeted politely by a youngster about nine years of age. I sneered at this child and treated him discourteously. I pushed this boy aside rudely and strode directly to the central hall where I challenged the Master.

"I felt then that I possessed enough 'knowledge' to defeat any master who would confront me, for I had already defeated many. But I was wrong. I relied on my dexterity, my 'knowledge,' and the old Master at once defeated me—swiftly, soundly, even easily. I then took a vow to become a novice in his school, but I did not live up to my word. In that failure I violated a cardinal ethic of martial arts, and since that time I have felt a horrendous shame that has obsessed me, followed me like a shadow.

"For the last twelve years I have reaped the whirlwind. I now realize that I alone am responsible for my actions." An-nan looked about the hall. "You have guessed who the Master was, and who the child. None other than Master Lam and Xuan here. Xuan who is now clearly my superior both in talent and in martial spirit." He bowed deeply once again to Xuan, who reciprocated modestly.

"I sympathize with those among you who have suffered poverty in childhood. My own childhood was such a one, and I am only now able to begin to recover from its negative moral effects. I cannot blame those effects, but only ascribe them to my *karma*, for now I understand the Path. I summoned up all my courage and went to Master Lam and confessed my misbehavior and sought from him a possible solution for my life's misery. I have followed his advice and, despite the ravages the change wrought in me, I have now begun to be able to tame my unruly mind." An-nan smiled. "The April showers have brought forth the May flowers. I hope you have understood and can forgive my 'lecture.'"

The group was silent, although each felt like applauding An-nan's heartfelt narration.

Henry spoke, "Teacher An-nan, your account reminds us that in the West all of us generally show off and rely too much on words. We live on our 'outsides' and grow little on our 'insides.' We are proud of our mastery of dialectics and do not realize that, as Master Lam has shown us, self-realization is not the product of dialectics. Self-realization is not knowledge, or what one does—but what one becomes.

"I remember how a classmate told me years ago that he would not be able to graduate with his class because he was short a three-unit required class. I must laugh as I remember, although my laughter is ironic, for my classmate's required class was ethics! He needed to throw on that ethics overcoat the following semester in order to be graduated.

"Then I thought about that matter again in the light of our role as martial arts teachers. I remembered Master Lam telling us that the consciousness of ethics must be stimulated and begin its growth in our earliest years, as children. We can plainly see that we have a lot of work to do."

All considered Henry's words and he continued, "Soon we shall bid each other farewell and return to our own schools, resume our daily work, teach our own system. I have but a single wish for us all, and that is that we all put into daily practice Master Lam's valuable teachings. In so doing we shall maintain the rightness of our arts and at the same time benefit our children and our communities. As for me, I shall follow that direction for the rest of my life. How about you?"

Xuan closed his eyes and nodded his agreement, a smile on his face. The Master's message is truly life-affirming, he thought.

Cheerfulness suffused every countenance, and it seemed that love and mutual understanding joined every heart. With shining eyes Xuan stretched out his arms, seeking the hands of his companions on either side. Kneeling there together in their circle, all joined hands spontaneously and, like an army reunited after battle, they felt powerfully victorious, conquerors of themselves.